Understanding
Depression

Liz MacLaren

BROCKHAMPTON PRESS
LONDON

This edition published 1996 by Brockhampton Press, a member of
the Hodder Headline PLC Group

ISBN 1 86019 346 3

Printed and bound in India

Preface

This book has been written by a lay person for other lay people. Its purpose is to give members of the general public some information about depression so that they will be able to identify the condition in family members or friends, should it occur, and so that they will then be able to seek professional help for them as soon as possible.

Since depression is a commonly occurring disorder, and since it is no respecter of persons, it is in all our interests to become better informed about the condition so that we are in a better position to recognize the early stages of depression, not only in others but in ourselves, should it strike. Early diagnosis and early professional help can do much to reduce the stress that depression brings.

Lack of knowledge and education about depression among members of the public is a cause of concern in those professionals working in the field. It is as a result of this concern that a campaign to defeat depression by circulating information about it was launched by the Royal College of Psychiatrists and the Royal College of General Practitioners. As part of this campaign, a leaflet was published giving information about various aspects of depression, and this leaflet is referred to throughout this book.

The book emphasizes the importance of early diagnosis and the importance of professional help. It also emphasizes the optimistic side of depression—the fact that the condition is, in a great many cases, eminently curable. It deals with some of the problems associated with depression, such as the difficulty of diagnosis, and also deals with the symptoms and suggested causes of the condition as well as the various treatments used to cure or alleviate it. Basically, the book aims to reduce our level of ignorance of depression, which is the greatest ally of depression.

Contents

Chapter 1

Depression—What Is It?

At any one time, about three million people in Britain are suffering from depression. Each year nearly four thousand people in Britain kill themselves while suffering from the most severe form of depression. These are alarming statistics, but even more alarming is the fact that about one-third of people who suffer from depression do not have the condition diagnosed and so do not receive any treatment, despite the fact that depression is eminently treatable.

This is because of the lack of knowledge that exists about depression. In 1992 the Royal College of Psychiatrists in association with the Royal College of General Practitioners launched a five-year campaign, called Defeat Depression, to increase public awareness of the condition and to make people better informed about the symptoms, causes and treatment of depression.

Educating the public about specific medical conditions often meets with great success. Given the fact that depression is difficult to diagnose and that it can lead to suicide if it is not diagnosed, we all have an obligation as human beings to find out more about this distressing condition.

Depression is a subject fraught with problems and uncertainties. These relate to every aspect of depression, from symptoms to diagnosis, to treatment, to aftereffects, but they begin with the very word itself.

The main problem in relation to the word 'depression' is that it is a word commonly used too loosely and too generally to be an effective description of what is in effect a mental illness, in some cases a very serious mental illness. In its loose general sense it simply indicates a lowering of the spirits, which may be extremely temporary and extremely minor.

Other members of the word family associated with the word 'depression' are also used loosely and generally—indeed, even more so. Thus if it is a rainy, dreary, dark November day when neighbours pass in the street, it would be quite common for one of them to say to the other, 'What a depressing day!', simply meaning that it is not the kind of bright summer's day when everyone bounds around full of the joys of life.

We are even more likely to toss around the word 'depressed' loosely and even lightly. Children can be said to be 'a bit depressed' because a party has been cancelled, or shoppers might admit to being 'rather depressed' because they failed to find what they were looking for on a shopping trip to town.

The very fact that we can say with truth from time to

time that we are depressed, in that we are feeling slightly down or less happy than is our usual state, makes it difficult for us to grasp that some people who are depressed are suffering from a severe illness. If we have a cold we can appreciate that people suffering from tuberculosis or pneumonia are far more seriously ill than ourselves because the difference in the severity of the symptoms is reflected in the name. In the case of depression, the name is the same for a minor, short-lived state of mind and for a mental illness that can become very serious and can last some considerable time.

To people who have recently been depressed in a medical sense, this trivial use of the word bears no resemblance to what they have in fact felt. It is by no means unusual for people who have been suffering from depression and who are in the recovery stage to vow that they will never use the word 'depressed' lightly again, having had no idea of what horrors the word could convey until they actually became depressed themselves.

Inevitably, as recovery becomes complete and memories fade, they do find themselves using the word in the way that the rest of us do. Old habits die hard, and it is a good thing that their own perception of depression does not dominate their lives.

The problem with depression—the medical condition—is that it is much more than the lowering of the spirits suggested by the general use of the word 'de-

pression'. Some people who have suffered from the
condition feel that 'despair', 'abject despair' at that,
describes the condition more effectively than the word
'depression' ever could, and even then it is an underestimation of the feelings of hopelessness and blankness
that depression can bring.

The medical profession obviously is not unaware of
the linguistic problems associated with depression and
has made some attempt at remedying the problem by
ascribing the term 'clinical depression' to the medical
condition known as depression. As far as the geneal
public is concerned, this is no great improvement because it does not really convey anything very much to
the lay person. It certainly does not add anything to the
average person's perception of what depression is.

Depression is all about how the people suffering
from the condition are feeling inside and how it affects
not only their moods but also their mental powers and
attitudes and their way of looking at people and things,
especially themselves. People who have experienced
the condition at some point in their lives are the best
people, in my view, to describe depression. This is not
necessarily true of all conditions, but I think that it is
true of depression.

IMAGES OF DEPRESSION

Depression has been variously described by people
who have suffered from it. 'My blank-wall days' was

how a friend of mine once retrospectively described the
period of depression in her life before the condition
was diagnosed and before she was hospitalized.

She could remember quite clearly going into work
and being quite unable to do anything else but stare
blankly at the wall or into space. Whole days were
passed in this way, with nothing seeming to impinge on
her consciousness.

This description is certainly evocative of the feeling
of utter blankness and oblivion that can accompany depression. A sense of emptiness is an associated feeling
also described by some who have suffered from it.

Spike Milligan, one of the best-known comic gen-
iuses of the twentieth century, is quoted as referring to
such emptiness in *Depression And How To Survive It*
(1993) by Spike Milligan and Anthony Clare. In a report of a conversation with Clare, who is a psychiatrist,
on how depression makes him feel, Milligan replies,
'There is this terrible emptiness. I just want to go away,
disappear, cover myself up until it goes away.'

These images of blankness and emptiness go a long
way towards describing the experience. They do not,
however, capture the sense of utter despair that is associated with depression, especially in its later stages if it
goes untreated.

The black dog

Winston Churchill (1874–1965), British prime minister, is said to have described depression as a 'black dog' following him, and others also have used this description. Samuel Johnson (1709–84), the writer and lexicographer once wrote to his friend Mrs Thrale about his own particular 'black dog'. 'The black dog I hope always to resist, and in time to drive, though I am deprived of almost all those that used to help me.'

He went on to comment on the constant presence of his 'black dog', metaphorically referring to the relentless nature of depression. 'When I rise my breakfast is solitary, the black dog waits to share it, from breakfast to dinner he continues barking.'

To those who like dogs, and black dogs in particular, this seems too friendly a concept for something as terrible and threatening as depression. A more oppressive image is necessary to describe the condition adequately.

Depression has also been likened to a black bird, such as a crow or a raven. The suggestion is that one of these rather sinister birds is perched on someone's shoulder just waiting to pounce and bring despair.

Both Winston Churchill and Samuel Johnson suffered from regular bouts of depression, and in fact both the image of the black dog and that of the black bird have tended to be used by people who suffered from such a condition rather than by someone who experienced a single bout of depression, or at least rare bouts of depression.

The black tunnel

A 'black tunnel with no light at the end of it' is an apt description given by several people who have suffered from a period of severe depression. It conveys succinctly and vividly the feeling of despair, emphasizing as it does the absence of light and hope.

Recovery from depression, by whatever means, does not happen overnight, although in most cases it does occur. It is essentially a gradual process, especially if the depression has gone undiagnosed for some time.

Some who have recovered speak of the immense pleasure and relief that they felt when they first saw a chink of light at the end of their own particular tunnel, when they first began to believe that perhaps they could be cured. It contrasted sharply with the deep black tunnel in which they had been living.

The dungeon

Blackness and darkness are inextricably associated with depression. For some, the relevant image is not a tunnel but a dungeon, a dungeon from which there seems to be no escape, as though, having incarcerated there the person suffering from depression, the jailer had lost the key.

Again, as with the chink of light beginning to manifest itself at the end of the tunnel, people in the early recovery stages have spoken of the supreme joy at glimpsing some light breaking through. It is as though someone has lifted the lid or door covering the top of the dungeon.

Spike Milligan emphasized this sensation of loss of light as well as that of total emptiness in his conversations with Anthony Clare, which are referred to above. He movingly describes depression as 'this black void, this terrible, terrible, empty, aching, black void.'

A dense fog

I have also heard those who have recovered from depression, or from a bout of depression, liken the state when they were ill to some dense fog in which they were irretrievably lost and which bore relentlessly down on them without any light getting through. It was described to me once by someone who had suffered from a period of depression and who lived on the east coast of Britain as being like the sea mist, called in Scotland a 'haar', that swirls in to the land from the sea and covers everything completely with its cold denseness, as though it would get into your very bones.

Throughout history there have been many creative people who have suffered from a depressive condition. Indeed, there have been so many of them that attempts have been made to show a causal connection between depression and the creative spirit, and this aspect of depression is dealt with in Chapter 4, entitled Depression—Causes.

Several writers have attempted to describe how this

condition appeared to them. The American writer Mark Twain (1835–1910) described the sense of hopelessness felt in the grip of depression:

'It is a time when one's spirit is subdued and sad, one knows not why; when the past seems a storm-swept desolation, life a vanity and the future but a way to death.'

MELANCHOLIA

Depression was formerly known as melancholia. This was recognized by the ancient Greeks as a disorder of the mood and was put down by them to an excess of melancholy, or black bile, in the sufferer's system, the word 'melancholy' being derived from the Greek *melas*, 'black' and *chole*, 'bile'. The Greeks believed that illness, whether physical or mental, was caused by an imbalance in the body of what were known as the four 'humours' or body fluids—blood, choler (yellow bile), melancholy (black bile) and phlegm.

The Greeks are thought to have known quite a bit about the symptoms of depression, in that it seems to have been associated with sleeplessness, irritability and an aversion to food. If that is the case, then it has taken a very long time to move farther on from that position.

FREUD

As with other aspects of mental disorders, it was not until the Austrian scientist Sigmund Freud (1856–

1939) came along that much progress was made as to the nature of melancholia or depression. In an essay entitled *Mourning and Melancholia* (1917), he emphasized features that are common to grief and depression, such as the despairing sense of loss and the lack of interest in the outside world.

DISCOVERY OF ANTIDEPRESSANTS

Probably the next really major event in the history of depression was the development of the first drug that was found to have antidepressant properties. In the mid 1950s Dr Roland Kuhn and his colleagues in Switzerland, while seeking a drug that would relieve psychotic symptoms, discovered a drug called imipramine.

Imipramine was found to be ineffective in calming psychotic patients. However, it was also found that depressed people who were treated with it experienced a raising of the mood and a relief of symptoms.

The drug belongs to a class of compounds known as tricyclic antidepressants (TCAs), which are still commonly used in the pharmacological treatment of depression. Indeed they are often the first treatment tried, and imipramine itself is still used.

While Dr Kuhn and his colleagues were conducting the research that led to the development of imipramine, research was also going on that was to lead to the discovery that another class of drugs, known as monoamine oxidase inhibitors (MOAIs), was useful in the pharmacological treatment of depression. Dr Nathan Kline and his team discovered that a drug called iproniazid, a member of the MOAIs, which was then being used in the treatment of tuberculosis raised the mood of patients and made them less depressed.

More information is given on the use of drugs in depression in Chapter 5, entitled Depression—Treatment. For the moment, the tricyclic antidepressants and the monoamine oxidase inhibitors are mentioned simply as a milestone in the history of depression.

It was natural that more would become known about depression as cures for it, or least for its symptoms, became available. People who had recovered from it were able to give information about what it was like to suffer from it. They were able to say how they felt when they were in the grip of depression and even to speculate on what might have led to their condition.

Thus doctors were able to glean more first-hand information about the condition. At the same time, research was, and still is, going on to reveal more about the nature and cause of the condition.

In view of the length of time that depression, or melancholia, has been identified, there is still much that is not known about it. The average person is still woefully ignorant on the subject of depression, but even specialist doctors working in the field admit to a lack of knowledge, particularly in relation to the causes of depression.

DIFFERENT KINDS OF DEPRESSION

There are different kinds of depression and different degrees of it. It is a mood disorder that can be thought of in terms of a continuum that runs from the blackest of suicidal despair to severe mania.

With reference to the nature of depression, various different kinds have been suggested. The major line that is drawn between different kinds of depression or mood disorder is that drawn between what is known technically as *unipolar depression* and that which is known as *bipolar depression* or *bipolar affective disorder*.

Lay people know unipolar depression simply as depression. They know bipolar affective disorder as manic depression.

Manic depression

Bipolar affective disorder, or manic depression, involves two different phases of mood disorder. These phases sometimes occur one after the other, and there is often a period of stability between the two extremes.

In one phase of the condition, the person suffering from it experiences the symptoms of depression, described in Chapter 2, entitled Depression—The Symptoms, and, in its extreme form, the state described earlier in this chapter.

In the other phase, the person suffering from the condition experiences an unduly happy or joyful mood,

to the extent of being euphoric, hyperactive and rest-
less, of showing a decreased need for sleep, increased
talkativeness, an inability to concentrate on any one
thing before going on to the next, racing thoughts, un-
wise expenditure, and other activities of that nature.

In other words, in the depressed phase of the condition the sufferer slows down to an abnormal and often
alarming extent. In the manic phase the sufferer speeds
up, also to an abnormal and often alarming extent.

One phase resembles a car whose battery is flat and
refuses to start, or at best starts only after much effort
or when jump leads have been used. The other phase
resembles a car that has gone out of control because its
brakes have failed, or a car that has a joyrider at the
wheel, who is obsessed with speed but has not yet
learnt how to control a car.

As has been indicated above, unipolar affective disorder is contrasted with bipolar affective disorder and
is what most of us know simply as 'depression'. There
are various degrees of it, including severe or clinical
depression and a kind of low-grade, chronic depression, sometimes known as *dysthmia*, literally 'mood
disorder'.

Reactive depression
In the case of unipolar depression, or depression, as
most of us would call it, there is sometimes an attempt
to categorize different types. The kind of depression

that seems to be triggered by, if not actually caused by, a traumatic event in life is sometimes known as *reactive depression*, and, especially formerly, as *exogenous depression*.

Reactive depression can be triggered by various events that cause distress or trauma. These include bereavement, marital break-up, car accidents, and sudden job loss. Reactive depression can also be a response to some form of serious illness, such as heart disease or a form of cancer, and may even be a response to a virus.

It can also occur in response to an event that does not in itself seem obviously distressing but involves some form of upheaval, such as moving house when the person involved has wanted to move house. The birth of a child, which is usually considered to be a happy occasion, can also bring on a form of reactive depression. This is usually known as *postnatal depression* and is dealt with below.

Endogenous depression

The variety of depression that seems to occur for no known obvious reason—and therefore has no identifiable trigger—is sometimes known as endogenous depression.

Perhaps because of its very nature, endogenous depression seems to be more likely to recur than reactive depression, although this, too, has been known to recur, even if the initial episode has been treated successfully.

Postnatal depression
The birth of a baby, which is usually considered to be a happy event, can have unpleasant consequences for the mother's mental health.

Some degree of mood lowering is common in the days following the birth of a baby. Between two-thirds and three-quarters of women who have just given birth suffer from what is known informally as 'the baby blues'. This takes the form of mood swings in which the mother can be extremely cheerful one minute and very tearful the next. This is thought to be a result of hormonal changes and usually lasts only about forty-eight hours.

Postnatal depression is a much more severe condition that usually becomes evident within six weeks of the birth but sometimes even later than this. The condition is thought to affect between ten per cent and thirty per cent of mothers and is marked by some of the symptoms that characterize unipolar depression or reactive depression. For example, the sufferer usually experiences sleep disorders and eating disorders, feels exhausted and unable to cope, and feels low in self-esteem and self-confidence. This, on top of the pressures that a newborn baby ordinarily brings, can seem too much to bear.

Another mood disorder associated with birth is puerperal psychosis. This illness is usually manic-depressive in type and is much rarer than postnatal depression. The condition is very severe and can lead to delusions that can make the woman try to kill her baby, herself or both.

Seasonal affective disorder (SAD)

One form of depression that has recently been identified is thought to be a result of seasonal variation and to be brought on by winter. This is called *seasonal affective disorder*, the name being frequently abbreviated appropriately to SAD.

People suffering from this condition tend, unlike people suffering from depression that shows no seasonal variation, to sleep more instead of suffering from a state of sleep deprivation, which is common in other forms of depression. They also tend to eat more instead of becoming completely uninterested in food, thereby gaining weight instead of losing weight, as is common in other forms of depression.

In addition to those features that are characteristic of seasonal affective disorder, the sufferer also experiences some of the more usual symptoms of depression, such as feeling miserable, extreme tiredness, lack of concentration, and so on. SAD varies greatly in severity, and many people who are not suffering from depression regularly have some of these symptoms in winter. For example, they may want to sleep more and eat more, particularly more carbohydrate, and have less energy. Indeed this is true of a great many of us.

Above, we have had descriptions from sufferers themselves about what depression means to them and we have seen how depression in some cases can be divided into categories. More light will be thrown on the nature of depression in the later chapters of the book, which deal with symptoms, causes and treatment.

Chapter 2

Depression—The Symptoms

One of the problems relating to depression is that it is difficult to diagnose. It is not like pneumonia, chicken-pox or a fractured leg, in which physical signs point to the condition. There can be physical signs relating to depression, but they are not always present and they do not always make themselves obvious on a visit to the doctor.

Given the fact that depression is so common in our society and that it so often goes undiagnosed, it is important that all of us should know something about the disorder in case we get it ourselves or in case our friends get it. A little knowledge could save a great deal of suffering.

OUTWARD SIGNS

Depression is a mood disorder that, in its extreme form, leads to an impairment of physical and mental functions. Because it is a mood disorder and because we have all at some point in our lives felt some form of what we know as depression, however mild that was, we would expect anyone suffering from depression to appear very sad and dejected.

This is, however, not always the case. People have been known to commit suicide in the grip of a severe depression and their friends have later claimed that the person in question did not seem in the least bit 'down'. Such a reaction may be due, at least in part, to a lack of observation or to the fact that most people are in a permanent hurry these days and do not always have the time to spot what is going on under their noses.

Nevertheless, it is true that people suffering from depression can appear to be their normal selves, at least for relatively short periods of time. This could be because their problems are all going on inside their heads or because they have made a supreme effort to hide their condition.

I spoke to someone who had had very severe depression following the sudden break-up of her marriage. She has a great many friends, many of whom tried to take her mind off her problems by laying on various social occasions. They knew that she had every cause to feel very down, but many of them claimed after she became ill that she had seemed, if not quite her old self, then certainly not someone who was depressed enough to be classified as ill.

The person in question accounted for this after her recovery. She explained that she, knowing that her friends were making substantial efforts to try to cheer her up, would make what seemed to her to be superhuman attempts to appear to be as much her old self as possible. Provided the occasions did not last very long she felt that she could just about succeed.

She paid a heavy price, however. When she got home she would go straight to bed in a state of utter fatigue. Her superhuman efforts had drained her of the little energy she had had in the first place.

If the depression goes undiagnosed and becomes more severe, it becomes increasingly difficult even to appear to function as normal. People suffering from severe depression simply feel unable to make any social effort and do not have the energy to attend social engagements.

This is why many people who are suffering from depression often try to cut themselves off from as much social contact as possible. They either do not answer the phone or take it off the hook, leaving their number permanently engaged. Their friends may well assume that they are always out or always on the phone, but this is far from the truth.

Frequently they do not answer the door. Sometimes, too, if they are in a particularly depressed state they do not open the curtains, a darkened room seeming to them to be simply an extension of the darkness that is inside their minds.

Thus the archetypal image of the depressed person

as someone always looking gloomy and miserable and even bursting into tears does not always present itself in reality. It is easy for the onlooker to be deceived.

Weeping fits

Despite this, weeping is often one of the early symptoms of depression and often one that can aid diagnosis. People who have suffered from depression often speak of having experienced bouts of weeping that frequently came on out of the blue. These would happen when they were on their own or in the presence of close family members, presumably because we are conditioned not to show our emotions in public.

Sometimes, however, it is weeping in a more public situation that leads to the depression being diagnosed. If a patient suddenly bursts out into a spontaneous and uncontrollable bout of weeping in a GP's surgery, the GP is often more likely to take the matter seriously and to realize that depression is involved than if the patient is simply trying to say what is wrong, often in rather a nonspecific way.

In the later stages of depression the picture can change, and people who have suffered from the condition sometimes speak of their inability to cry, despite feeling a need to do so.

Although it is often not possible to spot depression from simply looking at a person, some physical signs can be present that give a clue to the condition. Usually you have to know the person well to observe these signs and you have to know a bit about depression to be able to ascribe the signs to the condition.

Personal appearance

One of these signs relates to how the person is turned out. People who are severely depressed often neglect their personal appearance. They may wear clothes that are not appropriate to the occasion or situation, or clothes that are not quite clean. They may fail to comb their hair adequately, and they may even neglect their personal hygiene to the extent that their lack of washing becomes obvious to others.

Obviously, spotting this lapse in grooming not only depends on how well you know the person but on how well-groomed the person was to start with. If the person is careless about appearance in a non-depressed state there will probably be little change in the depressed state, although there may be a change of degree. On the other hand, if the person in a non-depressed state always looks immaculate, as though he or she has stepped out of a band-box with never a hair out of place, then a sloppy appearance in a depressed state will be noticeable.

A woman of my acquaintance, who always appeared very neat and smart, spoke of her surprise at looking through her wardrobe after recovering from severe depression. She found that she had put away a number of garments in a grubby or stained condition when normally she would never have let them get into that state in the first place, let alone put them away unwashed or uncleaned.

In depression there are a number of symptoms that can arise but do not always do so in all cases. One of these relates to neglect of personal grooming. As has been indicated in the previous paragraphs, this certainly does occur in some cases but in does not occur in all cases and sometimes occurs only in cases where the depressed person is in a fairly advanced state of depression. Depending on the person's general attitude to grooming, it can be one of the last things to be affected by the person's condition.

Eating disorder

Eating patterns can be upset by depression. In some cases people eat more than they usually do but in most cases people suffering from quite major depression lose interest in food.

Since it is possible for people to become severely depressed before the condition is diagnosed, their lack of interest in food can show in their physical appearance. They can become thin to the point of emaciation.

The lack of interest in food can become obvious to friends in ways other than by obvious weight loss, especially if the person affected formerly had a healthy appetite and a keen interest in food. If someone who formerly set to with a will with knife and fork begins to toy uninterestedly with food and push it around the plate, depression is certainly something to bear in mind as a cause, especially if there have been other signs, although this in itself obviously does not represent a differential diagnosis. Apart from anything else, eating disorders such as anorexia, which is also very common nowadays, can create the same impression.

Sweating fits

Some people who have had depression report that they suffered from sweating fits in the course of their depression. These were, of course, very obvious to their friends.

These are usually associated with panic attacks, which are more usually thought of as being a sign of anxiety and were treated with drugs that could relieve anxiety. However, Anthony Clare in the book *Depression And How To Survive It* (1994) indicates that nowadays the current evidence points to the fact that many panic attacks are in fact associated with depression.

Other symptoms that are characteristic of panic attacks, although these are naturally not obvious to an observer, include rapid, shallow breathing, a pounding heart, and sudden feelings of intense fear and anxiety.

Lack of interest and enjoyment

As well as showing a lack of interest in food, someone

suffering from major depression is liable to cease to show an interest in anything. Hobbies in which the sufferer was once enthusiastically interested go unattended.

Cinema buffs who never missed a new release have no idea what is on at the cinema if they are in a state of severe depression. If friends more or less force them to go in order to 'take themselves out of themselves', they betray little or no interest and cannot seem to concentrate.

Those who were once noted for the quality of their housekeeping, those who formerly ran houses that shone and gleamed with cleanliness and that routinely smelt not only of polish and cleaning agents but of the delicious odours of home baking and of the sweet perfume of flowers newly gathered from a well-kept garden, may well turn into the kind of people who totally neglect their house, themselves and the other people in it. This is of particular concern in cases of people who live alone, not because the standard of house care has declined but because the level of self-neglect may affect the health of the depressed person.

People who were formerly extremely interested in what was going on in the world around them no longer even glance at the newspapers that they once read so avidly. They may still go on buying them out of habit and they may pile them up supposedly to read them later. This attitude to newspapers may well be related to the marked decrease in concentration that people affected by major depression often experience, a subject that is treated later in this chapter.

When suffering from a major depression, people who formerly loved nothing better than a good gossip with friends no longer join in and no longer seem interested. They may still attend the social occasion at which such gossip is usually exchanged but their participation is either nil, minimal or at best forced.

Not only do people suffering from major depression lose interest in things but they also lose the ability to enjoy things, even things that gave them great pleasure when they were well, whether this be sex, food, sunshine or anything else. I have one friend who is a real sun-worshipper who deeply regrets not only the fact of having had depression but also that she had it during a particularly hot summer that she was entirely unable to appreciate.

Lack of sex drive

The loss of one particular form of enjoyment that someone might notice in a partner is the lack of enjoyment in sex. When people are depressed they tend to lose interest in sex and have a decreased libido.

Sadly, since neither the person to whom this has happened nor that person's sexual partner is likely to think of depression as the cause of the decreased sexual desire, this symptom of depression can have disastrous consequences for the relationship. The partner of the

depressed person can begin to feel rejected and even
look elsewhere for sexual pleasure, and the person feeling a lack of sexual interest may think that this is only
in relation to his or her partner whereas it is in fact a
general lack of interest in sex and unrelated to the partner.

Because of this sexual factor, depression can play a
major part in the break-up of relationships. The fact
that people who are suffering from depression are less
likely to demonstrate the same outward signs of affection that they were likely to do when they were well can
add to this unfortunate situation.

Personality change
The lack of interest is often accompanied by a lack of
animation, and sometimes the voices of depressed people become more monotonous than they have ever
been. This is obviously most remarkable in people who
were once known for their vivacity. When people who
were formerly outgoing, voluble, energetic and interested in everything around them seem markedly to become withdrawn, taciturn, inert and lacking in interest,
it is time for friends to consider at least the possibility
of depression.

As well as their voices often lacking the animation
that they once showed and sounding monotonous, people who are suffering from depression often look withdrawn and make less use of their hands and eyes, and

body language generally, in the course of conversation than they usually would.

Such people seem to have undergone a personality change, and the knowledge that such a change has taken place can be of help to doctors in making a diagnosis. GPs do not see all their patients on a regular basis—if they did they probably could not cope. Some of them they may see very rarely or even not at all.

Thus, if someone presents in a seemingly very withdrawn state it can be helpful to the GP, or indeed to a psychiatrist if psychiatric referral becomes necessary, to be told by a friend or relative of the patient that this is a complete change from the norm. By this stage in the depression the patient may either not realize that the change is obvious, although he or she may feel very different inside, or may not have the energy or motivation to convey the fact to the doctor.

Loss of sociability

When people are depressed they frequently cannot summon up the energy to go out and meet people, even if they have arranged to do so. Often they make arrangements to meet people and then cancel them.

It should be remembered that people who are suffering from depression not only feel too exhausted to do very much but also have very little interest in anything. They also no longer find enjoyment in things that usually brought them joy or pleasure. Thus meeting other people on a sociable basis is usually something that they simply cannot face.

If the condition goes undiagnosed and worsens, they may well not even remember to cancel such social arrangements. Should you find yourself waiting in a restaurant for someone who has neither turned up nor got in touch to cancel and you know that such behaviour is completely untypical of the person in question it is worth casting your mind over the rest of his or her recent behaviour. It may just be an odd lapse but, especially if the person does not get in touch to apologize or to point out that he or she was in fact waiting in a different restaurant, there having been some confusion, it may be a sign of depression if other behaviour signs point to this.

Loss of self confidence

A lack of self-confidence can be extremely noticeable in people who are usually positively brimming over with it. Such loss of confidence is often one of the signs of depression. People who formerly embraced any challenge in sight, and even sought these out, seem to become timorous and uncertain of their ability to perform tasks that are well within their capabilities.

This can have a devastating affect on their careers if their depression goes undiagnosed, especially in positions, such as management or marketing, where self-confidence is part and parcel of the job. In these days of unemployment and cost-cutting, people who are seen not to be performing as well as previously or as well as the job demands are all too often got rid of, supposedly as part of some redundancy plan, without anyone trying to find out what has caused the under-performance. Often any excuse to get rid of someone is grasped at.

If someone does seem to be losing confidence and doing so to a marked extent, especially to the extent that he or she is no longer coping adequately with the job, it would be an act of great friendship to try to get the person involved to seek help. Otherwise the consequences both to health and career can be dire.

Lack of humour

This personality change from the vivacious to the withdrawn is usually accompanied by a total reduction in sense of humour. One young man to whom I spoke mentioned that one of the reasons why he had realized that there was something wrong with his mother when he was a young adolescent was that she seemed to change completely before his very eyes and, most importantly to him at the time, no longer shared his rather zany sense of humour.

People who know depression from the inside will know why. When there is only numbness, blankness and misery in one's mind it is impossible to find things amusing or to comment on things in an amusing way. Just getting through the day is hard enough.

Irritability
Often people who are suffering from depression become much more irritable than they usually are. They
take to snapping at everyone, including their children,
and things that would not normally bother them one bit
make them fly off the handle.

Of course all of us get a bit irritable from to time for
one reason or other, often if we are extremely tired, and
it does not mean that we are depressed. Irritability can,
however, be an indicator of depression if it occurs in
conjunction with other signs.

Restlessness and agitation
People suffering from depression can appear very rest-
less or agitated. They may spend a lot of time staring
into space, but they may also have periods when they
keep jumping up and going away. When they are
present they frequently exhibit signs of agitation, such
as twisting or pulling their hair, wringing their hands or
rubbing their arms.

Again, some people may go through periods of agitation for reasons other than depression. However, agitation should be thought of in relation to depression if it
occurs with other signs that are symptomatic of the
condition.

Negative thoughts and feelings of worthlessness
Another feature of depression that can alert people to

the condition is the voicing of thoughts that are totally negative and pessimistic. This is particularly obvious in people who are usually resourceful, positive and optimistic in their attitudes.

As people who have suffered from the condition will testify, depression deprives the sufferer of energy and hope. As has been mentioned in Chapter 1, Depression —What Is It?, they feel as though they are lodged in a black tunnel with no light at the end of it.

This feeling manifests itself in the conversation of people who are in the grip of a major depression. If they are suffering from what has been described as *reactive depression*, i.e. a depression that seems to have arisen in response to some life event, particularly a traumatic life event such as the death of a close relative or friend or the break-up of a marriage, they may well have every reason to feel down, but it is their way of dealing with it that may seem unusual and often out of character.

An unusually negative or inert attitude to misfortune in someone should again alert his or her friends and relatives to the possibility that he or she is suffering from a major depression. If someone who is used to accepting what fortune chooses to hand out in a reasonably philosophical, positive or energetic way appears to be being completely cast down by some life event for some considerable time and cannot seem to bounce back from it with some form of positive or fighting action, then alarm bells should sound in friends and relatives.

Someone who has suffered from severe depression will testify to the feelings of inertia and despair that give rise to these negative thoughts. He or she will also testify to the fact that friends and relatives who are faced with such negative thoughts and statements find it difficult to cope with them because they do not understand the cause of them.

Worse, because they do not understand depression or its symptoms, they tend to think of the depressed person as lacking in backbone or moral fibre. They thus take it upon themselves to try to remind the person of the need for this moral fibre and of the need to fight back against what Shakespeare's Hamlet called 'the slings and arrows of outrageous fortune'.

They thus resort to such stock remarks as 'Pull yourself together!' or 'You must try to snap out of it'. 'Get a life!' is a more modern equivalent of these, and there are a number of similar phrases stated with the intention of calling the inert person to action.

The fact that people go on making these remarks when faced with people who seem to be incapable of action, and who seem full of despair at the futility of everything, is an obvious indication that much more of an effort is required to educate people about depression. The fact is that people who are suffering from severe depression feel such fatigue as well as such despair that any form of action either seems beyond their power or requires so much effort that it wears them out completely.

It is important not to become impatient with people who are depressed and who are constantly talking about their problems or expressing negative thoughts. It is even more important that friends should stay in touch with someone who is expressing negative thoughts so that they can provide that person with people who will listen to their problems. Isolation is all too common a feature of depression.

In the course of conversations that indicate negative thoughts, people suffering from depression not only reveal their inertia and their sense of hopelessness and despair but also a sense of their worthlessness in their own eyes. You might, for example, hear them speak of their inability to do their jobs.

If this is the case, and especially if the person concerned is a high achiever to whom doing well at work is a major consideration and who has, furthermore, always fulfilled this ambition, then alarm bells should ring long and loud. A sense of self-worthlessness is clearly present without there being any justification for this feeling.

Suicidal thoughts
Sometimes conversations that indicate negative thoughts go several steps further and indicate suicidal

thoughts. More information on the subject of depression and suicide is given later in the book, but in the present context it should be pointed out that we should forget what is in fact a myth—that people who mention or threaten suicide never carry out their threat.

In fact the statistics that link suicide and depression are alarming. In *How To Heal Depression* (1995), written by Dr Harold Bloomfield and Peter McWilliams, the authors indicate that fifteen per cent of all depressed people will commit suicide as a result of their depression and that two-thirds of all suicides are directly related to depression.

In *Depression And How To Survive It* (1994) by Spike Milligan and Anthony Clare, the authors indicate that four in every five seriously depressed people will be troubled by intense suicidal thoughts at some time during their illness and that about one per cent of all deaths in England and Wales are due to suicide. Other statistics are no more encouraging.

Many people indicate that they are having suicidal thoughts before they actually try to commit suicide. Sometimes they may refer to it in some way in the course of conversation, although we are not talking here about the sort of melodramatic statement made by someone on the spur of the moment just after learning about a fairly trivial piece of news.

They may not say in so many words that taking their own lives is on their minds but they sometimes take to describing a future in which they play no part. From their conversation it would appear that they have written themselves out of the picture.

People suffering from suicidal thoughts sometimes reveal their mood and intentions in ways other than words. For example, they may purchase a means of doing away with themselves, such as a rope, knife or gun, or go to the doctor to try to get some sleeping tablets with a view to taking all of these at once.

Sometimes they may manifest their sense of worthlessness and their suicidal thoughts in ways that seem to others sensible if they do not take the state of mind into consideration. Indeed they may even applaud them for their actions, not realizing what these actions might be leading up to.

One woman who had severe depression that went undiagnosed for many months about ten years ago following the sudden break-up of her marriage tells of how she went to her lawyer and made a will leaving all she had to her two children, while at the same time instructing the lawyer to transfer the guardianship of her children to her elder brother in the event of her death. The children were in their early teens and the woman was in her very early forties.

She says that she had not admitted even to herself that she was going to take her own life but she had been feeling for some days that she was not going to be around for very much longer and wanted the children to be safe and secure. In addition to her arrangements with her lawyer she had put all the rest of her affairs in order, despite the fact that ordinarily she was the kind of person who routinely lived in a state of chaos and never paid bills until the expiry of the final demands.

Fortunately this woman had a friend who was a doctor and who met her by chance after not having seen her for some time. He felt that her behaviour was worrying and was concerned about her state generally. He succeeded in getting her GP to refer her to a psychiatrist who arranged the necessary treatment for her.

After her recovery she says that she asked her lawyer if her behaviour had not seemed strange to him at the time. He replied that, on the contrary, her actions had seemed very sensible to him, despite the fact that her brother was quite a bit older than she was and the children were just a few years from the age when they would not have required a guardian.

The moral to this is obvious. Obviously, we do not all want to turn into alarmists, but it is worth noting what seems to be unusual behaviour in our friends or relatives, or at least behaviour that is totally out of character.

These then are the outward signs that someone is suffering from depression. It is important that we take steps to get treatment for someone whom we feel may be suffering from depression if this seems otherwise to be going undiagnosed and untreated. Too often we are wise after the event and realize that something was wrong only after the person has been hospitalized.

DEPRESSION FROM WITHIN

The thing about depression is that, for those unlucky enough to get it more than once, it is easier to spot the second time around. When people suffer from it the first time they often have no idea what is happening to them. The condition frequently comes on gradually and, although the person who is suffering from it can be all too aware that there is something far wrong, he or she often has no idea what it is.

After they recover from depression many of them indicate that they had experienced many of the symptoms indicated above as being indicators of depression that observant friends and relatives might pick up on and act upon. However, this is seen as retrospect and they were not sure to what extent they were aware of any of these at the time. Obviously, to some extent this varies from person to person.

Sleep problems

Doctors regard certain irregularities in former sleeping patterns as one of the cardinal signs of depression. Of the people to whom I spoke who had suffered from depression at some point in their lives and who had recovered, all spoke of experiencing sleeping irregularities during the period of time in which they were depressed.

For the most part, however, this was realized only retrospectively after they were better, partly because of information about the symptoms of depression given them by doctors in the course of treatment. They had not necessarily associated the sleeping problems with the rest of the way they were feeling and put it down to other things, such as worrying about whatever had brought on their state of mind in the first place. For example, people whose marriages had just broken up might think that their sleeplessness was caused by worry about the financial implications of this.

The most common kind of sleep irregularity associated with depression is characterized by an inability to remain asleep. Frequently people who are suffering from depression are so fatigued that they cannot wait to get to bed and fall asleep. This they often do but all too frequently they do not stay asleep.

Of course not all of us sleep like logs all through the night and never wake up until morning, but waking up in the middle of the night when suffering from depression is an entirely different thing from waking up in the night when one is perfectly well.

Almost invariably, people who are suffering from depression cannot get back to sleep when they wake in the early hours of the morning. Unlike people who are perfectly well, they do not have the energy or the inclination to get up and make a hot drink and they do not have the interest or concentration to read a book or listen to the radio. They just lie there worrying anxiously about all their problems and cannot switch off from these.

As the depression worsens and the sleep deprivation increases, the anxious thoughts also get worse. In fact they often not only become negative thoughts, which have been discussed above as being likely to become obvious in conversation with others, but become doom-laden. The very worst possible scenarios, with the most disastrous outcomes, present themselves in the early hours of the morning to the depressed person longing for sleep.

Other sleep disorders can also be a problem in depression. Sometimes the person suffering from depression suffers from insomnia and cannot get to sleep at all, despite feeling deep, deep fatigue. Other sufferers sleep for far longer than is normal for them and simply cannot get out of bed in the morning.

Nightmares

Nightmares do not usually feature in descriptions of depression, although they may be assumed to be covered by sleep irregularities. However, several people who have suffered from, and recovered from, depression mention nightmares as one of the things that they remember vividly about the period of their life during which they were ill.

Often such nightmares seem to involve some form

of darkness—dark clouds enveloping them, being lost in an impenetrable fog, being locked in dark rooms, wandering around homeless in the middle of the night in a blinding snowstorm, and others equally indicative of blackness and hopelessness. The nightmares seem to mirror the kind of feelings that the depressed person is experiencing when awake.

Feelings of misery and despair

Obviously, people who are suffering from depression feel miserable and unhappy since depression is a disorder of mood. It is not simply the kind of sadness that most of us know because this is often relatively transient and it is rarely all-consuming.

In depression this is not the case. There the misery is long-lasting, there seeming to be absolutely no end to it. It is also very deep, and there is no question of anyone simply 'snapping out of it'.

Nothing seems to relieve it, for the person suffering from it, as we have seen earlier in the chapter, has no interest in things that were formerly of great interest and does not enjoy any of the things that formerly brought great pleasure. The misery is unrelenting.

Especially in the earlier stages of depression it is quite common for depressed people to feel worse at one particular time of day than they do for the rest of the day. For many people this time of the day is the morning.

This is bad enough. If the condition goes untreated, however, these feelings of unhappiness get much, much worse and become feelings of despair and desperation. It seems to be the latter feelings, rather than the feelings of misery, that are most remembered by people who have suffered from depression after they recover.

When people are suffering from this kind of despair everything seems as black as it possibly can be. Admittedly the situation in which depressed people find themselves can actually be very bad by any standards, for example, from the financial point of view, but in their depressed condition they lose their resourcefulness and ability to think of solutions to problems.

They simply view the whole thing as having the worst possible outcome and seem incapable of doing anything to prevent this happening. The situation is worsened by the fact that, in the face of this seemingly unavoidable doom, depressed people often feel worthless and can even feel as if anything bad that happens is directly attributable to themselves. Thus feelings of worthlessness and guilt are added to feelings of misery and despair.

These feelings can lead to people thinking that there is very little point in going on in such a state of misery. They begin to feel that they cannot live in a world so devoid of hope, and they begin to have suicidal thoughts of the kind referred to earlier in the chapter.

Pain and numbness

Some people who have suffered from depression speak of experiencing great inner pain when they were depressed. As the condition worsens, however, this can become sheer numbness, and some sufferers speak of having experienced a void inside them. They speak of reaching a state in which they did not seem to be able to feel anything at all when they were suffering from very severe depression.

One woman refers to the fact that in the most severe phase of her illness, just before she was diagnosed and began a course of treatment, she not only could feel no inner pain but her ability to feel physical pain was impaired. She speaks of burning herself when taking something out of the oven and of seeing a blistered arm without really having experienced anything much in the way of pain. It was as though all her responses, both physical and mental, had been dampened down.

Fatigue

We have seen earlier in the chapter how observant friends and relatives can detect depression in the changed behaviour of the depressed person. Loss of interest is one of these observable changes.

Depressed people themselves often remember experiencing this lack of interest while they were ill after they have recovered, but to many of them it is not such a vivid memory as that of the fatigue that they experienced. This would have prevented them from doing very much even if they had had any inclination so to do. They simply had no energy.

Those who have experienced the kind of fatigue that frequently accompanies depression claim that it was far worse than any kind of tiredness that they had ever experienced before. It has been described as a state of exhaustion that permeates the whole body completely.

While people are in such a state of fatigue they may find it too tiring to carry out the least taxing task. Going to buy a few articles at a shop can seem like a trip up Everest to the person contemplating the outing.

Considering that the fatigue is often accompanied by impairment of memory, loss of concentration, indecision and even mental confusion, it can reach the stage when all everyday tasks seem insurmountable.

Feelings of helplessness

Combined with the fatigue and the unrelenting misery, depressed people often also suffer from feelings of extreme helplessness. They can be in very bad situations that normally they would make a determined attempt to deal with. When they are severely depressed they frequently feel that the worst possible outcome is inevitable, that there is nothing they can do to avert it.

Feelings of worthlessness

Depressed people often become extremely lacking in

self-esteem. Their feelings of helplessness and fatigue exacerbate this, and the lack of self-esteem can become so bad that the depressed person thinks that the world would be better off without him or her. A terrible consequence of this can be the suicidal thoughts referred to earlier in the chapter.

Feelings of guilt

Depression often, although not necessarily, arises in response to some unfortunate, unlucky or traumatic life event. Frequently this event is in no way the fault of the person who becomes depressed.

Whatever the circumstances, many depressed people not only blame themselves for whatever event brought on their depression but for any other bad things that happen. They may even blame themselves for bad events that happen to other people when they could not possibly have been involved. For example they may blame themselves for a relative's heart attack, a friend's motor accident or a colleague's death.

Living with this burden of guilt can become intolerable and can easily lead to suicidal thoughts as the person affected by the depression feels that the world would be better off without anyone who has caused all the tragedies for which he or she feels responsible.

Loss of concentration

All of us have days when we feel that we cannot concentrate effectively for various reasons. We may feel tired, we may feel worried, the job in hand may seem extremely boring to us or there may be other things that we would rather be doing.

As a symptom of depression, loss of concentration is not a one-off lapse but a general, ongoing and usually ever-worsening condition. It is an aspect of depression that can have worrying implications both for the people suffering from the condition and for others.

Loss of concentration has enormous implications in the workplace. Practically all jobs require some degree of concentration, and some jobs require a great deal. In certain occupations loss of concentration on the part of someone can even put other people's lives at risk. Society needs to be aware of this, and it needs to be aware of the fact that loss of concentration is commonly a symptom of depression.

People who go on working when their powers of concentration are either vastly diminished or practically nonexistent can be a real liability if not an actual danger. Yet it is hardly ever their fault. Usually they have no idea what is wrong with them, and all too frequently they seek help, only to have this denied because the people whom they consult fail to recognize or diagnose their depression, perhaps because they do not appreciate that lack of concentration is a common sign of depression or because they do not realize the extent of the problem.

There is a very worrying problem with respect to loss of concentration and depression and the fact that it often goes undiagnosed. It is that people who have severely impaired concentration can not only be working but driving cars too, thereby putting others at risk as well as themselves.

Lack of concentration can become really bad in depression. People who have suffered from it speak of being unable to read a newspaper or magazine, of being unable to concentrate on the lightest programme on television, and of being unable to concentrate long enough to make sense of a letter.

Memory impairment

Difficulty in remembering things does not usually feature largely in descriptions of the symptoms of depression. Yet, quite often, people who turned out to be suffering from depression without having realized it speak after their recovery of the great concern that they felt when they began to realize that they were failing to remember things.

It is the kind of aspect of depression, of course, that will be most obvious in people who have good memories and who do not generally have to write things down in order to remember them. When people find that they cannot remember telephone numbers that they have known off by heart for years they naturally begin to worry.

They tend to worry even more if they forget appointments or arrangements that they have made, and indeed
such omissions can have important consequences in the
running of their lives. For example, if someone is suffering from severe depression, he or she can easily forget to attend an important work meeting or even forget
to collect children from school, nursery or child-
minder.

All of us occasionally forget something—we may
even forget a telephone number that we know well—
but when we begin to forget things on a regular basis
we naturally become anxious. It is common for people
suffering from depression to think that they are losing
their minds, and one of the things that leads them to
draw this conclusion is memory loss.

It is all too easy for them to misdiagnose the reason
for their forgetfulness. Nowadays, with Alzheimer's
disease having quite a high profile, depressed people
experiencing some loss of memory may wrongly think
that they are suffering from this. Even people who are
quite young may form this conclusion since it is made
clear in the media that Alzheimer's is not just a disorder
of the old.

Suicidal thoughts are mentioned in an earlier section
of this chapter. It unfortunately seems likely that if a
depressed person, already suffering from feelings of
despair and worthlessness and suicidal thoughts, then
begins to think that he or she may have a condition

characterized by an irreversible deterioration of the
mind, then the suicidal thoughts are likely to become
worse.

Indecision

In addition to memory impairment and loss of concentration, many people who have suffered from severe
depression speak of having memories of suffering from
great indecision. They found themselves quite unable
to make decisions about even the most trivial things,
and when they eventually did succeed in coming to any
decisions they usually changed them. They remember
making arrangements and then cancelling them, that is,
unless they forgot that they had made the arrangements
and failed to act on them.

Mental confusion

Yet another aspect of depression that seems not to be
given much prominence in descriptions of the symptoms of depression is that of mental confusion. The
failure to recognize this symptom may be because this
kind of confusion arises quite late on in depression and
perhaps is experienced only by those who are very severely depressed. Certainly it does occur.

Someone who experienced it in the course of severe
depression describes it quite simply as having had a
mind full of fog. Indeed, it seemed to this person like
the final straw after having already endured the on-

set of memory loss, indecision and lack of concentration.

The onset of mental confusion, especially when taken in conjunction with memory impairment, can lead depressed people to think that they definitely have some condition that has irreparably damaged their minds. Again, this can only exacerbate suicidal thoughts.

Suicidal thoughts

These have been referred to in an earlier section, also called Suicidal thoughts, in the chapter under Outward signs. Such thoughts have been described there because they often manifest themselves in certain forms of behaviour or in certain comments or conversations. For further details see that section.

The depressed person who is having the suicidal thoughts might not actually realize that he or she is having such thoughts and may not consciously have planned to commit suicide. However, his or her view of the world is entirely negative and since all that the depressed person can see or imagine is darkness then it is quite likely that he or she might seek the final darkness.

The feelings of misery, helplessness and guilt all contribute to these suicidal thoughts, as does concern that there might be something far wrong with the mind in view of the memory impairment, the loss of concentration and the mental confusion.

I spoke to a woman who some years ago had depression so badly that, when it was finally diagnosed, she was hospitalized and declared to be suicidal by the doctor. Yet her friends say that at the time she never mentioned suicide and she herself says that she never referred to suicide even to herself. It was simply that any pictures of the future that she conjured up never seemed to include her and that she was having nightmares and daytime thoughts about drowning and she cannot swim.

Physical symptoms

When people are suffering from depression they sometimes experience physical problems. Constipation and disorders of the digestive system such as heartburn and flatulence are quite common, as are persistent headaches.

Also quite common in people suffering from depression are aches and pains for which there is no obvious physical cause and that do not respond to treatment.

Sufferers from depression, who, because of their condition, are not thinking as rationally as they normally would, sometimes become convinced that some physical pain is in fact a sign of some serious illness that the doctor has either failed to diagnose or has diagnosed but not revealed to the patient.

Some sufferers from depression experience sweating fits as part of a panic attack. Panic attacks are now thought to be associated with depression, although these are more usually associated with anxiety. *See* Sweating fits under Outward signs above.

FORMS OF DEPRESSION

The symptoms described above relate to reactive depression or endogenous depression, which are described in Chapter 1, Depression—What Is It?

Other forms of depression also exist. One of these is known as *postnatal depression*, a condition, as the name indicates, that can occur after the birth of a baby. Another *is seasonal affective disorder*, usually abbreviated to *SAD*, which affects some people during the winter months. Both of these are discussed in Chapter 1.

The above forms of depression have only one phase, a depressed one, and are known technically as *unipolar depression*. A form of depression that has two different phases, one of which is a depressed one and one of which is a euphoric one, is known as *bipolar affective disorder*, better known to the lay person as *manic depression*. This is also described in Chapter 1.

Summary

The above sections on Outward Signs and Depression from Within between them cover the possible symptoms of depression. Not everyone who has depression, even severe depression, gets all these symptoms, and which ones people suffer from can vary from person to person.

Still, it is best to know about all the potential symptoms so that you can more readily spot the condition. Lack of knowledge of the symptoms of depression can lead to the condition going undiagnosed, thereby causing much unnecessary misery. Worse, it can also lead to people trying to kill themselves and even succeeding.

MEDICAL CAMPAIGN TO DEFEAT DEPRESSION

There is much concern among some of the medical profession about the lack of knowledge that exists among the general public about depression. Other drives to educate people about some illnesses have paid off. Most women, for example, now know a great deal more about women's health problems in general and about breast cancer in particular.

With health education in mind and the need to educate the general public in depression, the Royal College of Psychiatrists in association with the Royal College of General Practitioners launched in 1992 a campaign called Defeat Depression. In a leaflet published for the campaign are listed some common symptoms of depression. These 'certain characteristic symptoms that give you, your family or your doctor a clue that you need professional help' are as follows:

- a loss of interest and enjoyment in life
- a lack of drive and motivation that makes even simple tasks and decisions difficult or impossible
- utter fatigue

- agitation and restlessness
- loss or gain in appetite, with loss or gain in weight
- sleeplessness or excessive sleeping
- loss of outward affection, going off sex
- loss of self-confidence, avoiding meeting people
- irritability
- feeling useless, inadequate, bad, helpless and hopeless
- feeling worse at a particular time of day, usually mornings
- thoughts of suicide; these are very common in depression and are much better admitted to than covered up, as they are a certain sign that help is needed.

Chapter 3

Depression—Difficulties With Diagnosis

RAISING AWARENESS
Ignorance of patient
Usually, when we feel that we are not quite right, we have at least some idea of what might be wrong with us. We may not be right—we may either have overestimated or underestimated the severity of the disorder—but we usually know roughly where the problem lies. Indeed, we often have something visual or physical to point to as the focus of the problem.

This is not true of people who are suffering from depression unless they are fortunate enough to have known something about the condition before being affected by it. Even if they have this knowledge, it is possible that they may fail to recognize that they are in fact suffering from the condition unless they have had depression before.

Need for public awareness
It is extremely important for people generally to be

aware of depression and its range of symptoms. If they
have this awareness they are likely to be able to spot
the signs of the condition in relatives or friends. They
can then encourage people whom they feel may be suffering from depression to seek medical attention and to
make sure that they receive this.

It was to raise the public awareness of depression
that the Royal College of Psychiatrists in association
with the Royal College of General Practitioners
launched their Defeat Depression campaign in 1992.
The leaflet that was published at the start of the campaign sets out much information about the symptoms,
causes and treatment of depression in simple, nontech-
nical language, easily understood by lay people.

Books on depression

Often people who have a health problem that they wish
to know more about may indulge in a bit of self-help
and seek a book that may throw some light on the condition. Nowadays there are a great many books published on the subject of health and aimed at the lay person, and depression is no exception.

Unfortunately the very nature of their condition often prevents people who are suffering from depression
from seeking help from the shelves of their local libraries or bookshops. Even people who are real book-
worms lose their interest in books when they are depressed.

They usually also suffer from such fatigue that the effort of going to a library or bookshop is just not to be countenanced. Since depressed people usually experience a marked decrease in their powers of concentration, they will be unable to take in the message of the books even if friends purchase them for them and save them the effort of going to the bookshop.

However, these books on health can be very useful. If friends and relatives get hold of those concerning depression and read them, they are then in a position to help the people who are suffering from depression and may be able to help in the diagnosis.

PATIENT AND DOCTOR
Getting the patient to the doctor

Often depressed people, particularly those who are suffering from severe depression, require a great deal of encouragement to seek medical advice and make the trip to see a doctor. Apart from anything else, the state of fatigue and exhaustion that many of them find themselves in makes any trip seem an insurmountable task.

Then there is the indecision that often accompanies depression to be taken into consideration. The depressed person may promise to seek medical advice and may even make an appointment to see a doctor, only to cancel it. This process can be repeated several times, and often the only way to make sure that a depressed person seeks medical advice is for a friend or relative to accompany him or her to the doctor's, at least as far as the waiting room.

Diagnosis by GPs

Unless the depression is at an advanced stage and the depressed person tries to commit suicide and is hospitalized, the first port of call for someone with depression is usually a GP. Sadly, just getting a depressed person to visit a GP does not always guarantee a correct diagnosis or the dispensing of the relevant treatment.

Patient problems

Sometimes the failure to reach an accurate diagnosis of depression lies with the patient and with the nature of the condition, although there is absolutely no blame to be attached to the depressed person for this fact. As has been discussed in Chapter 2, entitled Depression—The Symptoms, the depressed person does not always appear to be deeply miserable, and so one obvious clue to the condition is not visibly present.

In addition, as has also already been discussed, a depressed person, at least before the condition becomes very severe, can make huge efforts to appear normal and cheerful in certain social situations, which a visit to the doctor can be construed as being. This effort makes the person extremely exhausted but the fact that he or she can assume this appearance of normal mood again deprives the doctor of a valuable visual clue.

The doctor's role in diagnosis failure

Sometimes the failure to diagnose the condition lies with the doctor. It would be foolish to believe that all doctors are infallible or that they are all equally skilled in all aspects of medicine. The realization of how common undiagnosed depression is and of how important it is to recognize the symptoms of it is a relatively recent one—hence the fact that the Defeat Depression campaign launched by the Royal College of Psychiatrists and the Royal College of General Practitioners dates only from 1992.

Recently, more emphasis has been placed on the necessity for an understanding of mental illness. Thus, doctors who have been qualified for some considerable time are less likely to be as aware of forms of mental illness, such as depression, as doctors who have recently graduated. This is likely to be the case unless the older doctors have kept up with recent medical developments, which many of them do not have time to do.

This is not to say, by any means, that older doctors will not spot depression, since the quality of the individual doctor obviously matters, as with any diagnosis. It simply points to the fact that older doctors tend to be less psychologically minded than their younger counterparts and may be considerably more at home with the diagnosis and treatment of physical conditions than they are with mental conditions. They thus tend to look for evidence of a physical condition first.

Physical symptoms as a red herring

This tendency to look for a physical basis for a medical condition is exacerbated by the way some depressed people first present their illness to a doctor. Because the patient may be suffering from some of the physical symptoms that can be associated with depression he or she sometimes concentrates on these rather than bringing up the subject of his or her state of mind and inner feelings.

He or she may, for example, mention the digestive disorders that are sometimes present in depression. The doctor may then spend time trying to find out the cause of these and in treating them. The doctor may, for example, send a depressed person who is suffering from major digestive discomfort for a barium meal. All this can take some considerable time and distracts the doctor from diagnosis of depression.

Alternatively, the GP may spend time trying to find a physical cause for the persistent headaches that are a common accompaniment to depression. Again this can be a time-consuming exercise and a largely fruitless exercise at that.

Furthermore, such searching to identify a cause for a physical condition, and indeed the subsequent failure to do so, can convince a depressed patient of the presence of a terminal illness, such as a particular form of cancer. As has been pointed out in Chapter 2, entitled Depression—The Symptoms, this conviction that they are suffering from a terminal illness is a possible symptom of people suffering from severe depression.

It is a very bad thing if a doctor, however unwittingly, adds to the depressed patient's conviction that he or she has some life-threatening condition by undertaking undue physical examination and tests. Given that severely depressed people are prone to suicidal thoughts anyway, it is likely that the conviction that they have a terminal illness may make these thoughts much worse.

Communication skills

Where depression is concerned, good consultation skills on the part of the doctor are particularly important. It is by using these that he or she will be able to elicit from the patient how he or she is feeling and so reach a diagnosis of depression. If these consultative skills are not of a very high standard this can lead to a failure on the part of the doctor to diagnose depression.

Nowadays there is more emphasis placed on the importance of communication skills than there ever was before. This is as true of medical schools as it is of anywhere else, as members of the medical profession have come to realize how important it is that they learn both communication and listening skills and that they lose their image of talking way above the heads of the average patient, using technical language that is not understood.

The time factor

Diagnosing depression is, however, not as easy as it sounds. It often takes a long time to get the patient to give any information that will contain a clue to the condition. Even experienced psychiatrists who specialize in depression can take the best part of an hour to be satisfied with their diagnosis of depression.

To some extent, the length of time it takes to diagnose depression depends on the nature of the condition. Depression, as we have seen, has a general dampening effect on people's feelings and minds. They thus tend not only to be low in spirits but also to be considerably less articulate and responsive than they are when they are well. This, added to difficulty in concentrating and in remembering things, and their sheer fatigue, is hardly conducive to a coherent description of their symptoms to doctors, let alone in a hurried consultation.

The fact that depression consists of such a range of symptoms—just one or two of the named symptoms might well not constitute depression—is a major factor in the difficulty of diagnosing depression. It can take a very long time to elicit all the symptoms and so to build up a picture.

Time is not something we tend to associate with GPs. Usually they have waiting rooms full of patients, and we feel guilty even about taking up the five minutes it takes to have our diagnosis of tonsilitis confirmed or to have our repeat prescription written out. It has been indoctrinated in most of us from childhood that doctors are busy people and that we must not take up too much of their time.

Then there is the fact that the average GP simply does not have much time to spend on each patient. For many, fifteen minutes would be about the limit. If the doctor spent as much time as it can take to diagnose the condition of a depressed patient the waiting room would be full of a great many very disgruntled people.

The GP can suggest that the patient come back at another time when more time can be scheduled. There is the problem, however, that the patient may have used up a great deal of effort and energy in psyching himself or herself up to go to the doctor in the first place and may not be able to repeat this. In addition, severely depressed people often suffer greatly from indecision, and they might well make another appointment and then cancel it. Alternatively, given that some form of memory impairment is also common in severe depression some people suffering from the condition might simply not turn up for a repeat appointment.

The normality factor

There is often a problem, which occurs mostly in cases of reactive depression, when the depression has occurred as a result of some distressing or traumatic event in the patient's life. It is a fact that some doctors feel that if their patients in such a situation seem to have a marked depressed mood, then this a perfectly normal reaction in view of their unfortunate circumstances.

They are often unaware of the severity of the misery and of the other symptoms that are accompanying this. Instead of treating the condition they are apt to give lectures on how the patients should 'pull themselves together', 'fight back' or 'snap out of it'. This often can occur when the doctor knows the patient really well.

The GP's lack of knowledge of the patient

Lack of time and lack of knowledge on the part of GPs can certainly hinder the diagnosis of depression, as can the inability of depressed patients to give a coherent and accurate description of what is wrong with them. A contributory factor in the difficulty of diagnosis of depression is the fact that, in general, GPs have a considerable number of people on their lists whom they hardly ever see. Some of them they may never have seen, especially if the patients have moved into the area only recently or have just moved to that particular medical practice.

We have seen in the previous chapter, entitled Depression—The Symptoms, how people frequently seem very withdrawn and lacking in animation when they are suffering from depression. This is especially marked in people who were previously very vivacious and expressive before they became depressed. The diagnosis of depression can thus depend to some extent on contrasting the before and after state of the patient.

Should the GP know the patient well, he or she will be able to detect the difference and may be able to ascribe the change to depression, especially if this contrast is backed up by other symptoms that are typical of depression. However, should the GP have seen the patient only very rarely, or even never, then he or she has no way of knowing whether or not the patient is always rather withdrawn and reticent, unless this is of such a marked degree that it cannot be ignored, and the diagnosis may well be missed.

Help from relatives and friends

Usually, and naturally, doctors like to see patients on their own without the interference of friends or relatives, the exception being young children. If, however, you have a friend or relative whom you think may be suffering from depression and you are aware that the condition is going undiagnosed, it is worth trying to accompany him or her on a visit to the doctor so that you can emphasize the change that has occurred in your relative or friend. You may incur the displeasure of a member of the medical profession, but if you do not accompany your relative or friend you may live to regret it. Which is the more important to you?

Anthony Clare in the book *Depression And How To*

Survive It (1994) says that it is reassuring that GPs are less likely to fail to diagnose patients who are really severely depressed. At the same time he indicates another problem with regard to the diagnosis of depression. He points to the fact that those severely depressed people who go unrecognized and undiagnosed by their doctors 'tend to show less overt evidence of depression, tend to look less depressed, and are much less likely to attribute their ill-health to depression'.

THE STIGMA ASSOCIATED WITH MENTAL ILLNESS

To add to the other problems associated with the diagnosis of depression, there is the problem that some GPs are not only not always very psychologically minded with regard to illness but are positively reluctant to diagnose anyone as suffering from any mental illness, including depression. They do not wish to associate their patients with the stigma of depression.

There still is a great deal of stigma attached to any form of mental illness in this country, although it is hoped that attempts to educate the public in this area will meet with success. At the moment there is a distressing tendency to assume that anyone diagnosed as suffering from a mental disorder is mad and will behave wildly and even dangerously.

At the moment there is a marked failure to realize that there are various forms of mental illness with various symptoms and varying forms of severity. There is also a tendency for people to be unaware that some forms of mental illness, including depression, are eminently treatable.

Employers and the stigma of depression

It is this scenario from which GPs may, sometimes even subconsciously, try to protect their patients. This is partly because employers are often affected by this stigma and are far from sympathetic towards employees who are suffering from mental illness.

Many of these employers are unlikely to be happy to keep open the jobs of people who have been signed off work as suffering from depression or any form of mental disorder and may look for reasons to get rid of them. They are even less likely to want people who have been hospitalized because of mental illness to return to work on their release, despite the fact that people suffering from depression often recover from the condition completely after treatment.

Because GPs are all too aware of the stigma that is attached to mental illness and of the likely attitude of a great many employees, they are reluctant to give depression as a reason for someone being off work when they are writing out the necessary medical certificate. People who have suffered from depression and who have been in this situation speak of receiving medical certificates listing such conditions as 'respiratory infection' when they knew that they were off work with depression. This, of course, simply adds to the feelings of stigma that are experienced by people who have depression.

Psychiatric referral

GPs often show a marked reluctance to refer patients to a psychiatrist, even if the patients seem quite mentally ill and the GPs themselves do not know what is wrong or how to treat the problem. This is partly because they themselves are mainly used to treating physical diseases, partly because of the stigma regarding mental illness, which has just been described, and partly because many GPs are naturally suspicious of psychiatrists.

This is extremely unfortunate since psychiatrists, being specialists in mental illness, are much more likely to diagnose cases of severe depression than GPs are. Sadly, many people who are suffering from severe depression see psychiatrists only if their conditions become so severe that they try to kill themselves and are hospitalized.

Public suspicion and fear

Relatives and friends, as well as GPs, can be affected by worries about the stigma of mental illness. It is quite common for them to try to dissuade people suffering from depression from attending an appointment with a psychiatrist, and the leaflet issued by the Royal College of Psychiatrists and the Royal College of General Practitioners urges family and friends not to say to the depressed person, 'You don't want to go to a psychiatrist—you're not mad!'

Many people are ignorant about the facts of mental illness, and they are afraid of it. They view with suspicion, and often fear, anyone known to be suffering from it and do not wish any member of their family or any member of their group of friends to be diagnosed as having a mental illness.

They prefer to think that their relatives or friends who seem to be withdrawn and generally unlike their usual selves are simply in need of a rest. Alternatively, they think that the depressed people are simply giving in to things, and they urge them to fight back and 'snap out of it', not realizing that, for people who are suffering from severe depression, this is simply not physically or mentally possible.

Chapter 4

Depression—Causes

Nothing in relation to depression seems to be problem-free, and the cause of the condition is no exception. Doctors agree that there is no one cause of depression, but after that the issue becomes more complicated. Various theories have been put forward, but the truth of the matter as yet is that no one is really sure what causes depression.

Doctors feel that when they know more about the causes of depression they will be able to diagnose it more quickly and more accurately and that they will be able to treat it more effectively. For the moment they are awaiting the results of further research, although Anthony Clare, in *Depression And How To Survive It* (1994), indicates that 'It does seem doubtful, however, that, except in a small number of cases, a single cause will be identified.'

POTENTIAL TRIGGERS

Perhaps the most seemingly understandable type of depression from the point of view of cause is that sometimes known as *reactive depression*. As the name indicates, this depression seems to occur in response to some event in our lives, an event that causes upheaval in our lives and usually distress. Something seems to act as a *trigger* that sets off the period of depression.

Such a trigger can be any of the major distressing events in life, such as the death of a close family member or a close friend, a particularly nasty divorce, or the sudden loss of a job that someone had thought to have for life, especially when he or she is at an age when there is little possibility of getting another job. The trigger, however, can also be something that does not obviously seem particularly distressing. For example, people have been known to suffer from depression, seemingly as a result of moving house or moving to a new job that takes them to a different part of the country, despite the fact that such moves were sought and welcomed.

This cause and effect relationship of trigger and depression is obviously too simple to be the full story. Not everything that leads to upheaval or trauma in our lives leads to a major depression. Some people suffer from the most appalling tragedies in their lives and never suffer from depression, while other people seem to develop depression as a reaction to one incident in their lives, while having withstood previous, much more traumatic, events in their lives unscathed.

The leaflet published by the Royal College of Psychiatrists in association with the Royal College of General Practitioners as part of their Defeat Depression campaign contrasts what would seem to be a 'normal' reaction to a distressing event with what happens in depression:

'It is quite normal to feel depressed after a *distressing event*, but normally we "work through" what has happened after a time, and come to terms with it. But sometimes such events lead to more serious and persistent depression from which we find it harder to emerge.'

'Last straw' element in depression

Some people feel that there is a multi-factorial element in the relationship between the seeming trigger, or distressing event, and the depression. They think that the depression might not have occurred if there had been only one distressing or disturbing event in the life of the distressed person, that the depression occurred in response to a number of unfortunate or disturbing factors, of which the seeming trigger was the final straw.

Thus, for example, someone may come through the nastiest of divorces without becoming depressed if everything else in his or her life has been going swimmingly and happily, but if the said divorce comes at the end of a series of disasters, or even mini-disasters, then it can be a very different story. All of us have a breaking point, and the story can end in depression.

Circumstances

The leaflet drawn up by the Royal College of Psychiatrists and the Royal College of General Practitioners as part of their Defeat Depression campaign points out that the circumstance surrounding people who experience distressing events can play a part in how the people respond to the events. The circumstances can affect the likelihood of the people getting depression:

'Circumstances at the time we are stressed play a part. If we are alone, friendless, have many other worries or are physically debilitated, then we may get seriously depressed where in happier times we could cope.'

Isolation

Not having people in whom they could confide was mentioned by several women to whom I spoke as being a circumstance that they felt had contributed to their depression after they had met with a life event that had caused them distress. It was not that they did not have friends but that the friends who lived near enough to talk to on a regular basis were not the kind of friends with whom they could discuss the personal issues and intimacies that they would have liked to discuss.

Several of them had such friends but, given the general mobility of people, these friends lived far away, some of them even abroad. The women who had suffered depression and who put this down at least in part to having no one suitable to talk to felt that telephone conversations, particularly long-distance ones, were not nearly so effective or so rewarding. Without someone understanding within close range to talk to they felt isolated.

Not surprisingly, people who have been unemployed for a long time are prone to depression. This can obviously be ascribed to loss of hope on the employment front, but it can also be ascribed at least in part to isolation. Unemployed people have lost the companionship of their work colleagues and yet often do not have the financial resources to stay in touch with people socially.

The situation is even worse among the homeless. Admittedly, there can be a degree of companionship among people who live on the streets, but it is essentially a lonely life and a life in which there is not much hope. It is hardly surprising that many homeless people are thought to be suffering from depression, although there will be people among the homeless who were depressed before they became homeless.

SOCIAL CAUSES
The responsibility of family and friends
Sometimes people who have suffered from depression have felt that, although they had friends and relatives in whom they could have confided, they were let down by these people. Friends and relatives who could have helped by listening to problems for some reason or other chose not to, and the depressed people again felt

isolated. This situation is true not only of people who are actually in the grip of depression but also of people who are in the process of experiencing some form of traumatic event that is thought to be a trigger of depressive illness.

These friends and relatives who do not take the time to supply a friendly ear or even a shoulder to cry on might feel that they cannot spare the time from their busy, fast-lane lives. Very possibly they might feel that they do not want to become too closely involved in someone's problems—not getting involved is something of a modern preoccupation.

This is particularly true of trauma related to relationship problems, particularly separation or divorce. People tend to say that they do not want to take sides and that there must have been faults on both sides. Very possibly they have not been asked to do this, just to take the time to listen or to have a conversation. Nevertheless, they have declined to do this and have left a close friend feeling isolated.

People who have experienced some traumatic event often feel the need to talk, as do people in the early stages of depression at least—later on they often become withdrawn. They often go over the same points over and over again without necessarily realizing this. Patience on the part of family and friends is necessary. It is important not just to sigh heavily and either walk away or insist on changing the subject.

The leaflet published by the Royal College of Psychiatrists and the Royal College of General Practitioners emphasizes the need for people to offer their services as listeners in cases where people are depressed:

'Family and friends often want to know what they can do to help. Being a good listener (and a patient listener if you've heard it all before) is very important.'

This advice has relevance for the family and friends of those people who have experienced the kind of traumatic event that sometimes seems to trigger depression as well as for the family and relatives of those who are experiencing depression itself. The leaflet emphasizes the need for spending time with depressed people and the need to encourage them to talk. Again this emphasis is relevant to the family and friends of people who are in situations that might be thought to trigger depression as well as to the family and friends of people who are already depressed.

Unfortunately there is no longer as much camaraderie as there once was in the average workplace. Some of this can be put down to the high unemployment rate and to insecurity of employment. Because of the ever-constant threat of redundandcy, there is often a dog-eat-dog competitive spirit in many workplaces rather than a desire to help each other.

In addition, many workplaces have considerably fewer members of staff than was formerly the case, and many people are working much longer hours. They are

thus less likely to stay and chat to colleagues or to go
out for a drink after work.

A feeling of isolation is thus thought to be connected
with depression, both as something that can exacerbate
depression and perhaps something that can be at least
part of the cause of depression. People who generally
live isolated lives might be thought to be particularly
affected, and this is discussed under Environmental
causes below.

Environmental causes
Some people who are conducting research into depression think that environmental conditions may well be
implicated in the onset of the condition. They think that
chronic social stress and financial hardship may result
in people who suffer from these social conditions going
on to suffer from depression.

Of course the issue is not as simple as this. Many
people experience the most terrible economic and social conditions without ever suffering from depression.
The likelihood is that the environment in which they
live might predispose some people to become affected
by depression but that there are other factors at play.

We have seen above that medical experts think that it
is important for people who are suffering from depression to have someone to talk to and someone who will
listen to their problems. It is also thought that having
close family or friends who can provide such a service

might help to prevent the onset of depression in people who are experiencing the kind of traumatic events that are thought to have the potential to be triggers for depressive illness.

Not everyone, by any means, has access to this kind of help. Many people lead very isolated lives as a routine part of their environment. For example, many people feel isolated in high-rise flats on the edge of town with few facilities. They may feel isolated if they live in a street in which everyone goes out to work each day and they do not.

Partly because of the pace and nature of modern life and partly because of higher rates of crime and violence, more of us 'keep ourselves to ourselves', as the saying goes. This is all very well if we have a close-knit group of friends or family members but for people who do not, this increases their sense of isolation.

GENDER
Gender bias in depression

Many mothers of young children feel particularly isolated if they are at home with young children all day. This sense of isolation is increased if they are single mothers with no partner to help with the burden of childcare, or even to help with financial burdens, and no partner to discuss things with. In addition, they may live in an area with little community life and poor transport facilities.

One of the most striking features of depression is that more women seem to be affected by it than men. It is thought that social and environmental factors may play a part in this difference between the sexes.

Again, isolation seems to play a part—the isolation of women at home with young children or the isolation that some middle-aged women can experience after their children have grown up and left home, sometimes moving a considerable distance away. The latter are experiencing the trauma that can accompany what is known as the 'empty nest syndrome'.

It is also thought possible that the role of women in society can result in them leading lives that are more prone to depression than the lives of most men, in that they often meet with more day-to-day adversity. For a start, women are traditionally more likely to be involved in the task of housekeeping.

This is not only in itself a task involving a good deal of isolation but it is a task that means facing up to and coping with the burdens of the family, often the seemingly impossible financial burden of trying to make ends meet without the means to do so. Every day can be an economic nightmare and a battle to keep the family surviving.

The status and role of women
The fact that until relatively recently women generally had a low status in society compared with that of men is

thought to have some relevance to the gender bias in relation to depression. Even now, of course, women often have jobs that are low both in social and economic status.

The new roles that some women play in society may also affect women's seeming predisposition to get depression. We have seen above that there may well be a multi-factorial element in depression, that people may well survive a number of traumatic events or a great deal of adversity without getting depression and then something seems to act as a last straw and seems to bring on depression.

It is easy to see that this could have relevance in the lives of many modern women. They may be running a home and be responsible for looking after children and yet have a high-powered and demanding job. This can occur even if the woman concerned has a partner, since not all that many men feel that they should play a part in looking after the home and children, preferring to retain the traditional male role, even if his wife or partner has a full-time job.

Juggling the pressures of a home and a job, and coping with the problems that can arise in relation to both of these is obviously just the scenario in which 'last straw' depression could occur. For example, the woman might encounter at the same time childcare problems, problems with a parent who can no longer live alone, while at the same time perhaps having to work increased hours in her job and cope with political infighting there.

The prevalence of depression in women over men seems to apply more to unipolar depression in its less severe forms. Certainly as far as the incidence of manic depression is concerned, there seems to be little or no difference between the sexes. It is also thought that any difference in the sexes with relevance to depression may be restricted to the less severe forms of it.

The role of the stiff upper lip

The issue of seeming gender bias in depression is further confused by the fact that men traditionally are the supposedly stronger sex. They are thus likely to feel that they must not show emotions of sadness and that they must not publicize any weakness by consulting a doctor about their inner feelings and mental states. They must demonstrate the stiff upper lip.

It is, therefore, highly likely that men seek medical advice when they are in a depressed state only when this is at a very advanced stage, perhaps even when they have made attempts on their lives. Perhaps this could account for at least part of the gender bias in depression.

The leaflet published by the Royal College of Psychiatrists and the Royal College of General Practitioners indicates that:

'It seems that women get depressed more than men.

This may be because men are less likely to admit their feelings, bottle them up, or express them in aggression or through drinking heavily, or because women may be under more stress, say from having to work and at the same time looking after a child.'

Child-bearing and depression
There are certain stages in the lives of women that seem to be more liable to involve depression than other stages of their lives or than the lives of men. Research has shown that depression during pregnancy is quite common, particularly during the first and third trimesters.

Childbirth is even more associated with depression. As has been discussed in Chapter 1, entitled Depression—What Is It?, a mild form of this, called informally 'baby blues', is very common in the few days after the birth of a child. This usually passes quickly but *postnatal depression*, also quite common, is a much more severe disease and can take up to six weeks or even longer to make itself obvious. More information is given on this in Chapter 1.

The menopause
Depression is also sometimes associated with the menopause. It is recognized that the menopause is a crucial time in the life of women and that many people might feel depressed at the fact that they know that

their child-bearing years are at an end, a circumstance that might well be seen as a potential trigger for reactive depression. Also, they might feel depressed at the rather unpleasant physical symptoms, such as sweating fits and hot flushes, that often accompany the end of menstruation, in the way that people can become depressed in the course of a chronic, incapacitating illness.

Although this is the case, there is some dispute as to whether the menopause itself is a cause of depression. It has been suggested that it is likely that there is no intrinsic connection between hormonal changes occurring at the time of the menopause and depression, although oestrogen deficiency at the time of the menopause has been put forward as a possible cause of depression in women at that time.

PMT
Many women speak of feeling low in spirits in the days leading up to a menstrual period. In the worst of cases they may be suffering from severe premenstrual tension, or PMT, one of the affects of which can be an increased tendency to depression.

PSYCHOLOGICAL FACTORS
As has already been pointed out, little is known for certain about the causes of depression. From Freud onwards, suggestions have been made that depression can

be in some way related to certain occurrences in the early lives of people who go on to suffer from the condition. These occurrences include an unhappy childhood, bad relations with either parent or both parents, rejection experienced in childhood, child abuse, and other unpleasant experiences. This theory of depression often centres on some form of loss in childhood.

Personality factors
The leaflet on depression published by the Royal College of Psychiatrists and the Royal College of General Practitioners as part of their Defeat Depression campaign to raise the public awareness of depression indicates that personality may also have a causal role in depression:

'Personality may also play a part in depression. Although anyone can become depressed under certain circumstances, some of us seem to be more vulnerable than others, because of our individual make-up (including our body chemistry) or because of certain early experiences.'

This is not, of course, to suggest that some people who get depression are simply weak and dispirited by nature. Nor does it suggest that people who suffer from depression at some point in their lives have any obvious element in their personalities or characters that would lead anyone who knows them to suppose that they would get depression.

The core of our personalities are set in place very early in our lives, and it seems likely that any predisposition in our personalities to depression are related to the psychological factors described above.

The creative personality

It has also been suggested that there is something in the creative personality, if indeed there is such a thing, that predisposes people to depression. Colin Blakemore in *The Mind Machine* (1988) comments:

'Indeed, it seems very likely that creativity and affective disorders, especially manic depressive psychosis, are somehow linked. Saul, Nebuchadnezzar, Lincoln and Churchill; Coleridge, Hemingway, Sylvia Plath and Virginia Woolf; Handel, Schumann, Berlioz and Mahler: the known behaviour of each suggests that all experienced enormous mood swings typical of manic depression.'

Anthony Clare discusses the supposed connection between mental illness, and manic depression, and creativity and examines the evidence for and against the theory. He summarizes thus:

'Summarizing the evidence, the bulk of it favours a statistically significant association between mental illness and creativity, although there is a substantial minority report critical of the samples studied and casting cold water on the results.'

Clare goes on to state that it is manic depression that

is the mental illness that most studies seem to relate to creativity, there being little convincing evidence of a connection between schizophrenia and creativity, although some researchers have put forward this as a theory. He also raises the interesting point that the reason why there may be a connection between manic depression and creativity is that creativity is itself a form of illness in which 'the affected individual can express psychotic neurotic fantasies and preoccupations' whilst still remaining socially acceptable.

Psychological imbalance in thinking

It is usually thought that depressed feelings lead to depressed thoughts and a negative, pessimistic view of the world and what is going on in it. Some recent thinking, however, particularly that of Aaron Beck, puts this the other way round, claiming that depressed thoughts lead to depressed feelings.

This theory argues that the illness of depression is a disturbance of cognition rather than a disturbance of emotion. It argues that depressed people construe all their experiences in a negative way, tending to exaggerate problems and difficulties, view themselves in a negative way, considering themselves deprived, and survey the future in a negative, pessimistic way. In other words, it is thought that depressed people can have a distorted, negative way of thinking and so do not see things in perspective.

PHYSICAL CAUSES
Physical illnesses
Some physical illnesses are thought to cause depression. Some of these are hormonal disorders and include myxoedema and Cushing's syndrome.

Some cancers, such as those that affect the bowel and stomach, can initially be accompanied by depression. In addition, the realization that they have cancer, such as breast cancer, can act as a trigger for the onset of depression in some people. Also certain chronic, disabling conditions, such as arthritis, disseminated sclerosis and Parkinson's disease, can lead to depression.

Depression can also occur after certain viral infections such as flu and glandular fever and often occurs as one of the symptoms of ME (properly, myalgic encephalopathy).

Postoperative depression
People who are recovering from the effects of surgery, often major surgery, are thought to have an increased tendency to develop depression.

Childbirth
See Gender bias above and Postnatal depression in Chapter 1, entitled Depression—What Is It?

Drugs and medical treatment
Some cases of depression seem to be caused by drugs

taken as medication. These include some drugs taken to reduce high blood pressure, some drugs taken to treat cancer, to control epilepsy, and to counteract allergies. Steroids can also provoke depressed reactions, as can some drugs taken to cure insomnia and some drugs used to treat Parkinson's disease.

Radiation treatment for cancer is also considered to be capable of causing depression.

Mania, too, can be caused by drugs. These include amphetamines, cocaine and thyroid extract. Treatment with antidepressants can also cause mania, especially in high doses.

Vitamin and mineral deficiency

A deficiency in some minerals, specifically potassium, calcium, sodium and zinc, has been linked with depression, as has a deficiency of vitamin B12.

Alcohol abuse a cause of depression?

It is by no means uncommon for someone to be found to be suffering from alcohol abuse and from depression. It is not clear, however, whether alcohol abuse causes depression or whether depression causes people to turn to alcohol in the hope of finding some relief for their condition. Certainly, alcohol is a depressant but, although the position is far from clear, a recent American study tends to suggest that depression tends to lead to alcohol abuse rather than the other way round

Changing seasons

In some cases of depression the condition seems to occur in the winter months. This can be quite mild, and
indeed a great many of us feel more down in the dark
days of winter than we do in the bright days of summer,
but it can also be quite severe. This depression, which
is either triggered by winter or exacerbated by it, is
known as *seasonal affective disorder*, often abbreviated
to SAD. Further information on this condition is given
under Seasonal affective disorder in Chapter 1, which
is entitled Depression—What is it?

Biochemical causes

It is thought by some scientists that depression can be
ascribed at least in part to a fault related to the chemical
balance of the neurotransmitters in the brain. This is
discussed by Colin Blakemore in *The Mind Machine*
(1988).

Neurotransmitters are chemical substances that are
released in tiny amounts at the endings of nerve fibres
as a response to the arrival of a nerve impulse. These
nerve impulses, or messages, are transferred from one
neurone, or nerve cell, to another, and the functioning
of the brain depends on these.

It has been suggested, to put it in the most basic
terms, that depression may be a result of too little
neurotransmission and mania a result of too much
neurotransmission. Specifically it has been suggested

that depression is due to underproduction of the chemicals serotonin and noradrenaline, and mania to the overproduction of these, particularly noradrenaline.

However, Anthony Clare, in *Depression And How To Survive It* (1994), expresses reservations about the neurotransmitter theory with respect to depression, commenting that:

'The supportive evidence is elusive and largely insubstantial. We do not yet understand the biochemical basis of depression and mania.'

He does, however, go on to point out that research based on finding a biochemical cause for depression has produced benefits in that it has provided the basis of the development of antidepressant drugs.

In *How To Heal Depression* (1995), the authors, Harold Bloomfield and Peter McWilliams, raise the question that if there is a biochemical imbalance in the brain that corresponds to the negative thoughts that are a central part of depression, then which comes first? Does a deficiency in the neurotransmitters lead to the negative thoughts or do the negative thoughts led to a deficiency in the neurotransmitters? Their reply is that it does not matter as long as antidepressant medication helps to restore the proper balance of neurotransmitters in the brain and that other appropriate therapy is given.

The fact that certain drugs have been successful in curing depression makes some people believe that there must be some connection between the chemicals of the brain and depression, but not enough is yet known about this potential connection.

Genetic causes

It has long been thought that there is a tendency for depression to run in families. The writer and lexicographer Samuel Johnson, who suffered from depression wrote:

'I inherited a vile melancholy from my father, which has made me mad all my life.'

In the 1960s studies of family histories found that if one pair of identical twins had depression there was at least a fifty per cent chance of the other one also having the condition, even if the twins had been adopted and brought up separately in different environments. Since then, efforts have been made to establish a genetic factor in depression.

Most studies have found that relatives of people who have suffered from unipolar depression have an increased tendency to develop unipolar depression compared with the rest of the population. The tendency for depression to occur in families seems to be more likely in bipolar depression, or manic depression, than in other forms of depression, and relatives of people who have suffered from bipolar depression have increased rates both of unipolar and bipolar depression.

Very recently scientists have come up with results that indicate that a genetic fault can make people more susceptible to depression. It is thought that about one in ten people who suffer from depression carry the genetic defect, which interferes with the normal working of the brain.

The researchers revealed that the fault occurs in a gene known as SERT (serotonin transporter), which plays an important role in the transmission of signals between nerve cells in the brain. Scientists studying part of this gene found that it was different in people suffering from depression than in members of the general population.

For the moment, scientists do not know how the variation in the gene leads to depression, and further research is being done to try to establish the nature of the link. Reduced levels of serotonin in the brain have been identified in people suffering from depression, and some antidepressant drugs, such as Prozac, work by increasing serotonin levels. *See* Biochemical causes above.

The establishing of genetic causes for depression is at an early stage, and we should not forget that people who are related often share similar environments as well as genetic patterns.

Chapter 5

Depression—Treatment

ENCOURAGING TREATMENT
Going untreated

The treatment of depression, and how effective that treatment is, to some extent depends on the nature and severity of the depression in question. For that matter, some bouts or episodes of depression, even quite major bouts, seem to be self-curative in that after a while they may go away by themselves.

Leaving the condition untreated, however, should never for one minute be even contemplated. For one thing, an episode of major depression may last for months and months, and during all that time the depressed individual is having to endure a great deal of misery and desperation. For another thing, the likelihood of that depression recurring if it goes untreated is very high.

In *How To Heal Depression* (1995), the authors, Dr Harold H. Bloomfield and Peter McWilliams, indicate that, without treatment, half the people who have had one major depressive episode will have another, and that after two episodes the chances of having a third episode are even greater. They also indicate that chronic, low-grade depression, if left untreated, can last for years, even a lifetime.

In the case of manic depression, they indicate that the condition simply gets worse and worse if it is left untreated, with both phases of the condition becoming more extreme and the shifts from one phase to the other becoming more sudden and more frequent.

Need for encouragement to seek treatment

Unfortunately it is quite common for friends, relatives and work colleagues positively to dissuade depressed people from seeking treatment. This is partly because they have no understanding of what the person is going through and regard him or her as giving in to adversity instead of trying to 'snap out of it'.

Instead of encouraging depressed people to seek help and treatment for their condition, many friends, relatives and colleagues are likely to say, 'Pull yourself together!' instead. This is not only due to a lack of understanding but to a fear of mental illness or a worry about the stigma that is all too often attached to this.

The attitude of many friends, relatives and colleagues gives all the more room for concern because the very nature of the depressed person's condition can militate against his or her ever summoning up the energy or ever reaching a sufficient degree of decisiveness to make an appointment with a doctor and thus seek medical advice. Depressed people need all the encouragement they can get to seek medical help if their depression has reached a reasonably advanced stage.

If their depression is at an advanced stage, depressed people can feel too much of a sense of despair to think that they can be treated and so are unlikely to seek medical advice and treatment of their own accord. They just do not believe that they can be helped or that things can ever get better, a view that if left unaltered for long enough may well lead to suicidal thoughts and even to suicide itself.

It is very important for the general public to become aware of the whole issue of depression so that they will know how to recognize it when they encounter it and so that they will know how to try to help people whom they identify as being affected by depression. If education of the public is successful, then friends, relatives and colleagues of people who show signs of depression will know that some form of treatment is necessary.

Hopefully, they will also know the importance of pointing out that depression is just an illness like any other illness. It is no different from having a broken leg, except that the broken leg is more immediately obvious, having a very visual symptom. It is important that the depressed person becomes aware of this.

THE IMPORTANCE OF TALK
Most people to whom I have spoken about depression,

whether they are people who have themselves suffered from depression, whether they are people who have had friends or relatives who have suffered from depression, or whether they are people who have been on the treatment, rather than the suffering, side of depression, have emphasized how important it is that depressed people have someone to talk to. Much of the recent literature that has been written on depression also points to the need for depressed people to talk to other people.

This 'someone to talk to' in advanced cases of depression may be a general practitioner, a psychiatrist, a psychotherapist or a counsellor, but it is important for depressed people to have someone to talk to at a less formal level. If friends and relatives take the time to have regular conversations with someone who is depressed or with someone who is on the verge of being depressed, then this might prevent the condition either from developing into a more severe depression or perhaps even from developing at all.

Talking to friends and relatives

The leaflet published by the Royal College of Psychiatrists and the Royal College of General Practitioners on depression stresses how important it is for people to spend time with someone whom they know is suffering from depression or whom they suspect might be suffering from depression. It also stresses the importance of being a good listener to someone in this situation and the importance of demonstrating patience. Depressed people can seem obsessed with their troubles, and it is all too easy for friends and relatives to think that they have heard it all before and to stop listening.

In *Dealing with Depression* (1984, revised edition 1995), the authors, Gerrilyn Smith and Kathy Nairne, write of the importance to the depressed person of talking to someone and of sharing his or her worries in order to avoid feeling more and more isolated. They indicate that talking to someone may not solve any problems but that it can make the depressed person realize more clearly what is wrong.

To demonstrate the importance to the depressed person of having someone to talk to, Smith and Nairne quote someone who has suffered from depression as she voices the importance of having someone who will listen to problems:

'My friends were helpful by just being there. They were supportive and they were prepared to let me rabbit on and on.'

Someone whom I know who was very severely depressed before having her condition diagnosed has a distinct memory of feeling a great need to talk to anyone at all because otherwise she felt that she drifted into oblivion. Many years after her bout of depression she still remembers saying to the nurses in the hospital to which she was admitted that she needed to keep talking in order to stay with them.

Smith and Nairne are commendably blunt about the need for a depressed person to talk to someone. They address the depressed person directly:

'The point is that when you are depressed you need to talk it out in order to survive. Your need is very important.'

They stress the need for persistence on the part of the depressed person to find someone who will listen, preferably someone who understands the need to talk and the importance of talking:

'You need to keep trying to talk until someone listens. Do not be put off by another person's busyness. If one person has not got the time, try someone else.'

The problem with the latter part of Smith and Nairne's advice is that it seems to depend a great deal on the persistence of the depressed person, who may lack the energy to look around for the right person to talk to. The advice is more relevant to someone in the early stages of depression, before fatigue sets in, or to someone who has already suffered from depression and who knows the signs. It would seem more appropriate to try to make us all aware of the symptoms and potential dangers of depression so that we can identify it if someone whom we know becomes affected with it.

The leaflet published by the Royal College of Psychiatrists and the Royal College of General Practitioners on depression also indicates that it is important for friends and relatives to reassure people suffering from depression that they will get better, that 'they will come out of the other side'. It goes on to say that such reassurance will probably have to be repeated several times because depressed people, by the very nature of their illness, are prone to worry and doubt. If this reassurance is to be conveyed adequately enough and often enough it is vital that friends and relatives keep the communication channels open.

Another issue that the leaflet raises with regard to keeping in touch with the depressed person is the possibility that he or she might become worse and start talking of not wanting to live or start hinting at suicide. If depressed people are having such negative thoughts it is important that they are communicating these to other people, rather than just keeping such thoughts to themselves.

It is also important for the people who hear remarks about there being no point in living or hear mention of suicide to take them seriously. Telling themselves old myths about people who talk about suicide never actually carrying it out is certainly not the answer, since this is far from being the truth.

Instead, they should try as hard as possible to get the person who has spoken about the pointlessness of life and the possibility of suicide to look at things in a more positive light. More importantly, they should make sure that the depressed person's doctor knows of the suicidal thoughts of the patient, if he or she is in the process of being treated. If the depressed person has not yet consulted a doctor, then it may quite literally be a matter of life or death that he or she does so as soon as possible, and it is up to the people who have heard the suicidal thoughts at first hand to do something about it.

Talking to someone who has been there before
Of great value to someone who is suffering from depression is the opportunity to speak to someone who has had depression and who has recovered from it. In fact, most of us will number such a person among our circle of family, friends and acquaintances without knowing it.

This lack of knowledge can be put down to several reasons. We might not have known the person at the time he or she had depression; we might not have been anywhere in his or her vicinity during that unfortunate period; the person might have been so glad to recover from the condition that he or she never referred to it again, or the stigma that often is attached to depression prevented his or her condition from being widely known about.

It is unfortunate that many people who get depression have within their immediate circle people who have had depression without being aware of it. I spoke to two people who had found those who had suffered from depression themselves of immense help.

In one case a friend of the depressed person knew

that a mutual friend, and an ex-next-door neighbour of the depressed person, had had depression several years before, although the person who was currently depressed had not known her then. The mutual friend arranged a meeting between the two, and the woman who had had depression was able to persuade the friend suffering from depression to seek urgent medical help. Knowing from bitter personal experience how indecisive depression can make one, she even accompanied her to a psychiatrist's office, something that was necessary because of the severity of the depression.

In another case, someone was suffering from depression so badly that she was hospitalized and was totally unable to accept any kind of reassurance that she would ever get better. She was a journalist and was visited by a colleague who was able to describe how ill she herself had once been with depression and how she had recovered and had been perfectly all right for years.

Of course, the person suffering from depression did not immediately become more cheerful, and she did have great difficulty at that stage in concentrating on what was being said to her, since she was very ill with depression. She did say after her recovery, however, that, as her mood lifted under the influence of medication, she found it a great help to realize that someone who was able to describe what she had been going through and was going through was in fact functioning perfectly well and happily.

Up until then she had assumed that she would never be able to work again, since she could not concentrate long enough to read a single sentence. Hearing that someone whom she knew, and someone who was engaged in a similar line of work to herself, had once reached such depths was of great solace to her, particularly in the rather slow initial recovery stage of her illness.

Talking to people who are depressed is important, no matter what stage their illness is at. Friends and relatives should not stop engaging the depressed person in talk just because he or she goes on to receive professional advice. They will still have roles to play.

As has been mentioned earlier in the chapter, people who are just experiencing the frame of mind that can lead to depression might even be prevented from experiencing the full-blown condition if they have people to talk to. If the condition does develop into full-blown depression, talk is also important, especially as a means to persuade depressed people to seek advice and treatment or as means to try to instil some hope into them. When they are in the recovery stage, talk is important as a means of convincing depressed people that they will one day be completely well.

PROFESSIONAL TALK

However hard family and friends try, people suffering from depression usually require professional help.

Sometimes this also takes the form of a kind of talk.

Anthony Clare in *Depression And How To Survive It* (1993) points out the difficulties that family and friends can face when they are personally and emotionally caught up in what can be the very desperate situation of a depressed person. He indicates that there may well come a time when 'the neutral yet sympathetic observations and responses of a doctor' are more appropriate than the reactions of people who are concerned but without training and feels that skilled counsellors and doctors are usually better at getting depressed people to agree to treatment.

Clare stresses the importance of 'having someone who is there, prepared to listen, willing to support, able to indicate that he or she understands'. He reflects that too often the value of this gets left out of a discussion of treatments and yet it can be of such value to a patient.

GP consultation

The family doctor is the first professional person that most people would consult if they were suffering from depression, or if they were suffering from something to which they could not put a name, as is often the case with depressed people. As has been discussed in Chapter 3, entitled Depression—Difficulties with Diagnosis, GPs do not always provide the friendly, helpful ear that depressed people need.

The reasons for this are several. Most commonly, the

GP may not have the time, or claim not to have the time, and indeed the whole family doctor system is based on doctors taking a relatively short time to see each patient.

If he or she takes an unusually long time with any one patient it can throw out the whole appointments system for the day and make for considerable queues in the surgery waiting room. Lack of time on the part of GPs is obviously a very real problem when it comes to acting as a sounding board but, as Anthony Clare points out, 'many find the time and as a consequence do much to ease milder forms of mood disturbance'.

Another reason why GPs do not always supply the talk facilities that many depressed people need is that not all GPs are gifted with good communicative skills. Nowadays quite a lot of emphasis generally is placed on the value of communicative skills, and medical training is no exception. The problem is that this emphasis on communicative skills is a recent one, and many doctors practising today had qualified before it came into being.

It would be extremely unfair to suggest that all doctors who have been qualified for some time are low in communicative skills. Many of them are extremely good, but it is a point to be borne in mind by relatives and friends if a depressed person seems not to be making much progress on visits to the family doctor.

The role of the GP in acting as a listener is often

made difficult by the fact that the depressed person is often not very communicative in a situation that does not involve a friend, and more especially if it is a formal situation that involves a figure of authority. It can sometimes be difficult to get a depressed person to talk, especially in cases of severe depression, and even more difficult to get him or her to get to the point coherently.

The leaflet on depression published by the Royal College of Psychiatrists and the Royal College of General Practitioners on depression indicates in the section on treatment that talking can be helpful. It does, however, point out the difficulty that many depressed people have in using talk as a form of therapy. Their very condition deprives them of the energy to do so and their interest in doing so, 'but exploring and confronting the possible reasons for being depressed takes energy and motivation, and it is difficult while depression is still severe.'

As has been mentioned in Chapter 3, Difficulties with Diagnosis, there are at least two other barriers in the way of a GP understanding the position and acting the role of good listener to someone who is suffering from depression. One of these is the fact that some GPs tend to be much better at diagnosing physical conditions than psychological or mental conditions. Another is that, despite some recent improvement, there is still a good deal of stigma attached to mental illness in general, including depression.

Specialist agencies and self-help groups

The leaflet published by the Royal College of Psychiatrists and the Royal College of General Practitioners suggests in the section on treatment that if the depression from which someone is suffering is connected with a specific problem then he or she should think of consulting a specialized agency. For example, if the depression seems to be related to the break-up of a marriage or relationship then the person suffering from the depression might find it helpful to consult Relate, formerly the Marriage Guidance Council.

The kind of help supplied by such specialist agencies can be useful, but it is relevant only in cases of mild depression or in cases in which the potential trigger for depression is present but the depression has not yet become full-blown.

An alternative possibility put forward by the leaflet is that the depressed person goes to a self-help group. Self-help groups have become very common recently and consist of people who get together because they have, or have had, some common problem. Those involved are not professionals, but neither are they members of the depressed person's family or circle of friends.

The idea is that people who themselves know what people are going through are the best people to help people who have a particular problem or people who are suffering from a particular disorder. It is felt that this is a valuable but informal way of people working through their problems in a friendly and understanding atmosphere.

Such groups cover a wide range of problems and disorders. For example, there are groups for people who have had stillborn children, groups for people who have had breast cancer, groups for people who have ME, groups for people who have eating disorders, groups for people who are suffering from various forms of addiction, and so on. The most famous group, and one that is much older than the others, is Alcoholics Anonymous, better known as AA, which was formed to help people who were dependent on alcohol to try to break the habit.

Many people who have attended such groups have found that they have helped them immeasurably. Self-help groups have relevance to depression in that people who have suffered from a traumatic life event that has the potential to trigger depression may avert the condition by joining a self-help group aimed at sufferers from such a life event. Of course, they have probably been helped by someone, such as a friend, relative, doctor, minister or social worker, into making the decision to join a group, finding the whereabouts of the group and getting up the courage to attend the group and to keep attending.

As far as self-help groups specifically formed for people suffering from depression are concerned, they are often not really relevant to people who are in the grip of depression for the first time unless the condition is in its very early stages. At that point most first-time sufferers have no idea what is wrong and so are unlikely to know what action to take. They are probably more useful to people who regularly suffer from bouts of depression or to people who are in the recovery stage of depression.

Regular sufferers may take comfort from the knowledge that they are not alone. They will also appreciate having the support of people who know what the condition is like.

People who are in the recovery stage are more likely to be convinced that their recovery can be completed if this is told to them by people who have first-hand experience of this rather than specialist doctors or well-meaning but uninformed friends. Setbacks in the recovery stage of depression are by no means unknown, and self-help groups could be exceptionally helpful in getting people through these and back on the road to recovery.

Counselling

People who need to talk and need help to cope with a particular stage of their lives or with a particular problem often nowadays turn to counsellors. Counselling is a relatively new form of therapy, having developed enormously in the past decade.

Gerrilyn Smith and Kathy Nairne in *Dealing with Depression* (1984, revised edition 1995) describe the role of a counsellor:

'The aim of a counsellor is to listen and try to understand what you are feeling and what you are trying to say. She will then feed back to you what she has heard in a way that shows that she has understood, without giving judgements or advice.'

Smith and Nairne are here writing about depression from a woman's point of view, hence the reference to 'she', but of course there are both women and men counsellors.

Many people who are suffering from depression, or from other problems or disorders, find that counselling is the best kind of therapy for them, if their condition is not too severe. They feel that they can talk about their problems and receive emotional support without the added dimensions that other forms of therapy can bring. For example, they do not have to try to understand themselves, as some forms of psychotherapy can encourage people to do.

Perhaps the biggest advantage of all to some people is that counselling allows them to retain some form of control of the therapy in a way that they feel other forms of therapy do not. Counselling is held to be the least intrusive form of therapy.

The problem with counselling is that it is extremely important that the person seeking help, whatever the problem or disorder, should feel totally comfortable with the counsellor. If this is not the case then the counselling is unsuccessful, and unsuccessful counselling is probably worse than no counselling at all.

There are, in fact, a great many counsellors around nowadays, and, unlike doctors, there are no official qualifications that people have to have before they set themselves up as counsellors. There are many training courses run throughout the country, and these are for varying lengths of time and, almost inevitably, of varying levels of quality and effectiveness.

Counsellors who have sufficient training and experience can become accredited by the British Association of Counselling (BAC). This organization not only specifies a code of practice and professional guidelines for its members but it will supply a list of local accredited counsellors in your area if you contact them. *See* Useful Addresses.

Some health centres and medical practices now have a counsellor attached to them as part of the services that they provide. Alternatively, they may be able to give information on accredited local counsellors.

One good way of finding a counsellor would seem to be by personal recommendation from someone who has consulted a particular counsellor and been quite satisfied. Even this, however, does not always work.

I have one friend who was extremely enthusiastic about a counsellor with whom she had had several sessions in the course of treatment for depression. Knowing that one of her friends was suffering from depression, she had no hesitation in recommending the counsellor to her friend. Unfortunately, she did not get on with the counsellor at all, perhaps because she is of a completely different personality type from her friend.

People who are depressed need help with finding the right counsellor. As has already been indicated earlier in the chapter, the very nature of the condition deprives sufferers of energy and motivation, and so help is needed to persuade them to try to find a counsellor. They may also need help to get over a failed counselling consultation, as such an experience can all too easily confirm the sense of failure that they may already suffer from as part of their condition.

Psychotherapy

Anthony Clare in *Depression And How To Survive It* (1993) divides the various forms of psychotherapy into three groups: supportive psychotherapy, re-educative psychotherapy and reconstructive psychotherapy.

Supportive psychotherapy

Supportive therapy aims to get the patient to function as well as possible, both socially and psychologically, in the face of any disabling condition such as depression. It aims at increasing the patient's level of self-esteem and self-confidence.

This kind of therapy is sometimes used almost as a kind of preventative therapy as it is used to help people cope with those life events that are known to trigger depression or other psychological illnesses, sometimes when these are still at the anticipatory stage. For example, someone whose partner has a terminal illness may be given such therapy.

It can involve the therapist talking over with the relevant person the feelings and thoughts that are likely to occur when the life event, such as bereavement, actually occurs and talking over the anticipated difficulties. The person undergoing this form of therapy is encouraged to express his or her emotions freely and to think and talk about what directions his or her life will take in the light of the life event. Efforts are made to minimize day-to-day responsibilities during the occurrence of the life event.

Supportive therapy can have important relevance to depression. It is hoped that it will help to avert the onset of depression in people who are known to suffer from depression or who are thought to be vulnerable in terms of depression because, for example, they come from a family with a strong history of depression. Such therapy would be valuable for people known to have a genetic tendency to depression, when research has been completed on the link between depression and a genetic fault.

This form of therapy can also be relevant to depression when people are receiving other forms of treatment and are waiting for this to take effect. Some antidepressants can take three weeks to have much in the way of an effect on depression, and the patient has to be kept going during this period. Supportive therapy can help to do this.

Re-educative therapy

As the name indicates, this form of therapy sets out to re-educate a person's way of acting and looking at things. The most common form of re-educative therapy at the moment is *cognitive therapy*.

People who are suffering from depression are extremely low in self-esteem, thinking themselves virtually worthless. They also show a marked tendency to blame themselves for everything, even for those things completely out of their control. In addition, they view the world and the future with pessimism and despair.

All of this is usually an entirely different way of looking at themselves and the world than that which they have when they are not in a depressed state. The fact that they see themselves and the world in such a gloomy and pessimistic way points to the fact that their thinking is distorted in some way and that their view of reality is impaired. Whether a negative way of thinking is a symptom of depression or whether thinking negative thoughts makes one depressed is not clear, although the former is now thought to be the case.

Cognitive therapy, the founding father of which is Aaron Beck, aims to put right this distorted and pessimistic way of thinking. Its goal is to break the cycle of repetitive negative thoughts that are such a characteristic of depression.

The word 'cognitive' refers to how we perceive and think. The way in which we perceive the world dictates the way in which we respond to it. If our perception of the world is negative and pessimistic then our thoughts and actions will be correspondingly negative and pessimistic. Cognitive therapy tries to identify a person's distorted perceptions and aims to put them straight.

It tries to allow the depressed person to see things as they really are instead of through dark glass all the time. It does not aim to give the depressed person an unduly cheerful or optimistic view of the world.

Cognitive therapy is obviously not an overnight way of curing depression. Obviously, it is a slow process taking several sessions over several months, usually about three months since no one can retrain someone's way of looking at things in a short time.

At present it is thought that cognitive therapy can be effective in the treatment of unipolar depression when this is either mild or of moderate severity. It has not been found to have much effect in the case of very severely depressed patients until the severity of the condition has been lessened by some other means, usually drug therapy. Nor has it been found to be very effective in the treatment of manic depression, or bipolar affective disorder, as it is known technically.

Reconstructive psychotherapy

Reconstructive psychotherapy delves much deeper than re-educative therapy into depression and aims to get at what is the root cause of how the person is feeling. The most common form of this is psychoanalysis.

In psychoanalysis the psychoanalyst gets the person undergoing analysis to express his or her thoughts freely as they occur and then interprets and analyses these. Based originally on the theories of Sigmund Freud about the unconscious processes of the mind, psychoanalysis aims to explore a person's inner consciousness and find out about early experiences and how these might have affected him or her in later life.

The patient does most of the talking in psychoanalysis, but the psychoanalyst plays an important role. Much of the exploration of the person's inner world and how it interacts with his or her experiences in the outer world and of the exploration of what are believed to be different parts of the self are channelled through the relationship between therapist and patient. The patient transfers emotional attachments that he or she has had in the past, say with a parent, to the therapist, this process being known as transference.

Psychoanalysis is very time-consuming and therefore very expensive. Very frequent regular sessions are recommended, ideally five times per week, and each session should last fifty minutes, although briefer periods are being experimented with.

Many think that psychoanalysis is not a particularly effective way of treating depression, but the whole question of the effectiveness or otherwise of psychotherapy in the treatment of depression is one that fuels much debate. Part of the problem is that testing a therapy is extremely difficult on a global basis, given the number of possible variables associated with the testing—the personality and training of the therapist, variation in technique and in the circumstances in which the therapy is carried out, the personality of the patient, the severity of the patient's condition, the role of time or coincidence in the patient getting better, seemingly through therapy, and so on. Then there is the difficulty of deciding what represents success in therapy.

Interpersonal psychotherapy

Interpersonal psychotherapy is a simpler, short-term form of psychotherapy. It does not concentrate on the past and past relationships but on the present and present relationships. Emphasis is placed on communicative skills and on ways to improve the depressed person's relationships with others.

Developed initially by Myrna Weissman and Gerard Klerman, interpersonal psychotherapy was designed specifically to treat cases of moderate to severe unipolar depression. Its aim is to help the depressed person identify, understand and resolve difficulties that they have encountered in coping with other people and in relating to other people.

Anthony Clare in *Depression And How To Survive It* (1993) summarizes findings on the relative merits of forms of psychotherapy:

'Psychotherapy is helpful in severe depression but only in association with antidepressant medication. Cognitive forms of psychotherapy and reality-based interpersonal forms appear superior to psychoanalysis or psychoanalytically derived forms of psychotherapy.'

Finding the right therapist

There is no statutory registration for psychotherapists. Virtually anyone can claim to be a psychotherapist, however little training he or she has had.

However, there is now an organization called the UK Council for Psychotherapy, which has a voluntary register of psychotherapists, known as the National Register for Psychotherapy. In order to be listed on this register, anyone setting up as a psychotherapist must belong to one of the member organizations that follow certain guidelines and certain training standards and also have a stated complaints procedure.

Sometimes psychotherapy is available on the NHS. If you have been referred by your GP for psychotherapy there is a strong possibility that a particular psychotherapist will be recommended by your doctor, although some choice may be given.

Psychiatry

Psychiatry is at the other end of the talk scale from the informal chat by relatives. It often, of course, does not only involve talk, or a form of psychotherapy, but the use of medication.

People are referred by GPs to a psychiatrist when they are uncertain about the diagnosis of a patient who seems in some way to be mentally disturbed. They may also refer patients who are not responding to treatment for depression or for whatever mental disorder that they think is involved. Relatives may insist on a psychiatric opinion if they are concerned about the state of someone's mental health.

Perhaps the most common reason for psychiatric referral relates to the severity of the condition. People who are severely depressed and who have either tried to commit suicide or who have been having suicidal thoughts are often referred to a psychiatrist and are often hospitalized for their own safety until treatment can take effect. Indeed, people can be hospitalized against their will if they are thought to be a danger to themselves or others.

Psychiatry and stigma

The stigma that is attached to mental illness has been discussed elsewhere. This stigma is even stronger when it is attached to psychiatry. The leaflet published by the Royal College of Psychiatrists and the Royal College of General Practitioners advises family and friends of depressed people against making statements such as, 'You don't want a psychiatrist—you're not mad!'

Certainly, people are often dissuaded from consulting a psychiatrist or going into a psychiatric hospital or unit by relatives who do not wish them to be stigmatized. This can be extremely unfortunate, or even lethal, as people who have been referred for psychiatric help are often suicidal.

MEDICATION
Antidepressant medication
So much for the various forms of talk-based treatments for depression. Now let us turn to pill-based treatment.

Medication for depression often receives a bad press. This is partly because lay people tend to get tranquillizers and antidepressants mixed up. Until relatively recently, it was common for doctors to prescribe tranquillizers such as Valium rather too liberally for anyone suffering from stress or anxiety. It was then discovered that Valium is addictive, and people who had been on it for some time experienced unpleasant effects when coming off the drug, a process that had to be carried out gradually.

In fact antidepressant drugs and tranquillizers are completely different types of drugs, although it was by no means unknown for a GP to treat someone suffering from depression with Valium, thinking that the patient was suffering from anxiety or stress rather than depression. In fact, some antidepressant drugs do have a slight sedative effect, although this is not their main function. Most importantly, antidepressants, unlike Valium, are not habit-forming or addictive.

Apart from the unfortunate fact that they have quite wrongly been confused with Valium, antidepressants tend to receive a bad press. There has been a general move away from thinking that medicine is the answer to all our ills, and with this a move towards various forms of alternative medicine, such as homoeopathy, herbal medicine, acupuncture, aromatherapy, etc. This has resulted in an accompanying distrust of medication, whether this takes the form of antibiotics, antidepressants, or whatever.

If this were not enough bad feeling against antidepressants, more is created by the fact that some people claim that drugs simply numb or suppress the feelings and that by taking drugs to make us feel better we are less likely to face up and deal with what is wrong in our lives. They claim it is better to experience the pain and work through it than to take something to alleviate it.

In fact the numbness referred to is much more likely to be true of tranquillizers than it is of antidepressants. Antidepressant medication is designed to lift the mood and do away with oblivion and numbness.

Because of the feeling that is conveyed that people who take medication are in some way opting out of pain, although in the case of depression what they are often opting out of by taking medication is numbness, people often feel guilty about taking medication. This can add to the feelings of guilt that depressed people often feel as one of the symptoms of their condition.

Not only might they not take medication in the first place, but even if they agree to do so when they are very ill, they may decide to come off their medication too soon, when they begin to get better and become more aware of social pressures. Friends and relatives who do not understand the need for antidepressant medication, or who do not understand the way in which it works, often encourage people to come off their antidepressant drugs too soon because they have been subjected to the bad press relating to antidepressants.

It is under these circumstances that the leaflet on depression published by the Royal College of Psychiatrists and the Royal College of General Practitioners urges family and friends of people being treated for depression to try to help them to accept their treatment. It urges family and friends not to say, 'I wouldn't take the tablets if I were you.'

It is a pity that antidepressants receive such a bad press because many experts agree that drug therapy is the most effective form of treatment in cases of severe depression. People who are suffering from depression have enough to contend with without being made to feel guilty about accepting a form of treatment that is going to get them well again.

The people whom I have met who have suffered from severe depression at some point in their lives and recovered all indicate that antidepressants played a major role in that recovery. They felt that it was only after the drugs had begun to work that their mood lifted sufficiently to allow them to begin to think normally again.

In their book *Dealing with Depression* (1984, revised edition 1993), Gerrilyn Smith and Kathy Nairne, the authors, although they express reservations about drugs being dished out too readily, admit that there are occasions when antidepressant drugs can be helpful. They quote a few people who have found antidepressants useful. A remark in one of these quotes is particularly telling in relation to the role of antidepressants in the treatment of depression. It is made by someone who admits that she felt guilty about taking antidepressants but took them all the same:

'But I have often owed my continued functioning to those tablets and on more than one occasion agreeing to take them has kept me out of hospital.'

Different kinds of antidepressants

Until recently there were two main kinds of antidepressant drugs, the tricyclic antidepressants and the monoamine oxidase inhibitors. To these has recently been added another range called selective serotonin re-uptake inhibitors, of which the best known is Prozac.

Tricyclic antidepressants

These were discovered thanks to the research of Dr Roland Kuhn and his fellow researchers in Switzerland, who were really looking for a drug that would relieve psychotic symptoms in people suffering from severe mental illnesses, such as severe schizophrenia. The research team developed in 1956 a drug called imipramine, which was found not to be effective against psychotic symptoms. It was, however, found to make depressed schizophrenic patients less depressed.

Imipramine is still used today in the treatment of depression, as are other members of the group of drugs to which it belongs. Tricyclic antidepressants are so called because they are chemically composed of three linked chains to which a side chain is attached. The members of this antidepressant group of drugs do not vary greatly in terms of their therapeutic effectiveness, although to some extent they have a different range of side effects.

The tricyclic group of drugs is often still considered to be the first line of attack against depression in terms of medication. They are thought to be particularly effective in helping patients whose depression is accompanied by physical symptoms such as severe sleep disturbance or loss of appetite. Indeed, patients often speak with gratitude of being able to sleep normally on taking the drugs some time before they are aware of any lightening of their mood.

Time factor
One of the problems with this group of drugs is that they usually take between two and four weeks to take effect. This can present problems for people who are very severely depressed and, if they are having suicidal thoughts, it is highly possible that they will have to be hospitalized during this period. Not so severely depressed people, but people who are still quite badly affected by the condition, may benefit from cognitive therapy or interpersonal therapy during this period.

Also, it can take some time before the appropriate dose of the relevant drug is established. Sometimes the doctors start with a fairly low dose and have to increase it. To some extent the relevant dosage depends on the severity of the condition.

Unfortunately, because of the length of time that it can take before there is any obvious improvement in mood and outlook, the depressed person who is taking the drug can become disheartened and stop taking it before it has had a chance to start taking effect. This is even more likely to happen if the person has been suffering from one of the rather unpleasant side-effects that can accompany some of the tricyclic drugs.

Side-effects
These are more likely to occur in the older forms of the tricylics, such as imipramine or amitriptyline, than in the more modern forms. The side-effects can include a dry mouth, blurred vision and constipation. They can also include a sedative effect that can be of value if the depressed person is also suffering from agitation.

In fact, many people find that if they persist with the tricyclic drugs the side-effects disappear in a short time. Obviously, however, the problem is that some people are not prepared to wait for these to pass, particularly if they are not severely depressed.

Once the depression begins to lift, many patients feel they should be able to stop taking their antidepressant pills. These have to be tapered off gradually, however, rather than stopped suddenly. Moreover, it is thought that the pills have to be continued for some considerable time in order to avoid a relapse in the patient.

The older tricyclic pills are avoided in the treatment of the elderly. They can induce what is known technically as postural hypotension. In other words when someone taking the drug stands up his or her blood pressure can fall suddenly and sharply. The tricyclic drugs can also cause abnormal heart beat rhythms.

Overdose
Another problem with the tricyclic drugs is that they are more lethal if an overdose is taken than other drugs.

An overdose of ten times the recommended dose can lead to death.

Monoamine oxidase inhibitors

This group of drugs is so called because members of the group inhibit or slow down the process by which the enzyme monoamine oxidase breaks down the neurotransmitters that are thought to play an important role in the maintenance of a normal, balanced mood.

They were discovered in 1956 when Dr Nathan Kline at Rockland State Hospital discovered that a drug called iproniazid, which was being used to treat tuberculosis, had an effect on the mood of patients to whom it was administered. Kline began to give it to people who were suffering from depression and found it to be effective.

These drugs are often used if the tricyclic range of drugs is found to be ineffective. The monoamine oxidase inhibitors or MAOIs, as they are frequently called, are often used in cases of depression in which there are characteristics that are not thought of as being typical. These include anxiety, increased sleep, increased desire for food and a lowering of the mood in the evening rather than in the morning, which is the usual in cases of depression.

Side-effects
As is the case with the tricyclic range of drugs, the

MAOIs can cause some side-effects. These include headaches, dry mouth and constipation and, less commonly, blurred vision, agitation, sweating rashes and difficulty in urination.

Dietary and drug restrictions
People who are taking any of the MAOIs have to be careful what they eat and drink. They are supplied with a list of things that have to be avoided, a list that includes several cheeses, some smoked or pickled fish, red wines, and extracts of meat or yeast such as Marmite.

There are also certain drugs that have to be taken with care if people are already taking MAOIs and only after consultation with a doctor because of the interaction of the two drugs. These include cough mixtures, drugs used to treat blood pressure, antihistamines and several others.

This necessity to avoid certain foodstuffs and drinks is because they contain a substance called tyramine. The MAOIs prevent the breakdown of tyramine and a build-up of this in the body can cause a dangerous rise in blood pressure.

The dietary restrictions imposed by taking these drugs make patients likely not to continue with the prescribed course or to discontinue these as soon as they begin to feel better, although they should continue treatment for some time after this.

A newer form of MAOI, called RIMA, an abbreviation of reversible inhibitors of MAO-A has now been developed, and these are thought much less likely to interact with tyramine and so less likely to require such stringent dietary restrictions. The name of the new drug reflects that there are two forms of monoamine oxidase, named MAO-A and MAO-B.

Selective serotonin re-uptake inhibitors (SSRIs)

It has been suggested that depression can be caused by reduced levels of serotonin in the brain. The SSRIs, or selective serotonin re-uptake inhibitors, allow the brain to make better use of the serotonin that is in the brain by stopping its re-uptake into its storage place in the brain, thereby increasing the level of serotonin circulating in the brain.

Prozac

This group of drugs is quite new, and the best-known member of the group is Prozac, the brand name of fluoxetine hydrochloride. SSRIs are becoming popular because of their reportedly lower rate of serious side-effects. They are also considered to be safer than some other forms of antidepressants because it is difficult to overdose on them.

Prozac has been used in the United States for some time and for a shorter period time in Britain. It has been hailed as a wonder drug, and because of this many people, including many doctors, are suspicious of it. Many doctors thus prefer to stick to the older drugs, probably also taking into consideration that Prozac is considerably more expensive than the other forms of antidepressants in these cash-strapped days.

Side-effects
Although the SSRIs are reported to have fewer serious side-effects than the older antidepressants, they can have some side-effects, although these often wear off with use. The side-effects include diarrhoea, nausea, dizziness, headaches, dry mouth, nervousness, anxiety, insomnia and sexual problems.

Prozac should not be taken with any of the MAOI range of antidepressants. Taken together, the drugs can produce severe reactions, such as very high blood pressure, shock and nausea.

Prozac has had something of a bad press in the United States. People have claimed that it induces mania and aberrant behaviour, including violent behaviour towards others, and suicide, although the published facts do not support such claims

Lithium
Lithium is used in bipolar affective disorder, commonly known as manic depression. It is mainly used to try to prevent recurrence of the disorder in people who are prone to it and to treat acute episodes of mania.

Lithium is also sometimes used to treat depression that is resistant to other drugs, often in this case being used in conjunction with one of the tricyclic antidepressant drugs.

Lithium is not a synthesized drug but a naturally occurring element that is usually administered to patients in the form of lithium carbonate or lithium citrate. Lithium salts were used originally as a treatment for gout, and they were then used as a salt substitute for use by people suffering from heart disease. The salts are no longer used in either of these ways.

The role of lithium in mania was discovered accidentally by an Australian psychiatrist, John Cade, in 1949. He had originally thought that urea might be involved in the development of mania, and he injected pigs with lithium nitrate, a combination of uric acid and lithium, expecting that the uric acid would induce mania. Far from becoming manic, the pigs became lethargic. Cade wondered if lithium then would turn out to have a calming effect on the mood of people. He thus gave lithium carbonate to some patients who were suffering from mania and discovered that it had a beneficial effect

Time factor
Lithium has been found to be effective in preventing manic depression from recurring. Unfortunately, people have to take it for a considerable time, as long as a

year, before it works effectively. Because of this people tend to stop taking it, thinking it is not doing any good.

Since it is used to prevent recurrence of manic depression, lithium has to be taken for many years by people who are prone to the condition, and indeed some people may have to take it for life. Few of us like taking medication and taking it for a long time can seem a real burden, thereby leading many people to stop taking lithium, especially during periods when they are feeling quite well.

Side-effects
The side-effects that may possibly occur during the taking of lithium include unusual levels of thirst, increased urination, a metallic taste in the mouth, hand tremors, nausea and stomach cramps. These usually last only a few days after the beginning of the treatment.

Lithium may also affect the thyroid gland, making it underactive, and can result in weight gain. If taken in high doses it can cause kidney disorder or damage.

Electroconvulsive therapy (ECT)
There is generally a great distrust of ECT among the public. This is mostly because people often have an overdramatic view of the procedure, largely caused by literature or films. For example, in the film *One Flew Over the Cuckoo's Nest*, ECT is given without any form of anaesthesia to an unwilling and troublesome patient more as a form of punishment than as therapy.

ECT involves giving an electric shock to the brain and is thought to act by having an effect on the neurotransmitters that are believed to be involved in depression. It was discovered by an Italian researcher, Ugo Cerletti, in the 1930s when he was conducting research into a possible connection between epilepsy and schizophrenia, and was first used in 1938. Although it was not found to have any significant effect on schizophrenia, it was found to have a beneficial effect on people suffering from depression.

The use of drugs that paralyse the muscles for a very short time and of anaesthetic drugs that last for a very short time has decreased the amount of discomfort that people experience when having ECT administered to them. The process is considered by many to be effective in treating severe depression and has the advantage of working more quickly than antidepressant drugs.

ECT is used in severely depressed patients who have made serious suicide attempts or in severely depressed patients whose condition has not responded to antidepressants or who are unable to tolerate antidepressants. It may also be used in the treatment of elderly people who are suffering from depression because some of the antidepressant drugs are not suitable in view of potential side effects.

Side-effects
Common side-effects of ECT include headaches, mus-

cle aches and mild confusion. These usually clear up within a short time, although some patients report some loss of memory of remote events and some memory impairment generally for some weeks or months after the administering of ECT.

Light therapy

As has been indicated earlier in the book there is a form of depression that is apt to occur in the winter, called *seasonal affective disorder* and abbreviated to SAD. The discovery of this has led to the use of artificial bright light, known as phototherapy, as a form of treatment

This has been found to be quite effective but relapse is common when the treatment is discontinued. The light has to be several times brighter than the usual form of indoor lighting, and phototherapy has to be administered for at least two hours every day, preferably for four days.

Chapter 6

Depression—The Alternative Approach

The previous chapter deals with the usual mainstream treatments for depression. Nowadays there is a great interest in alternative or complementary medicine and therapies generally, and these are considered by some people to have application to the treatment of depression in its milder forms and in the avoidance of depression.

It should, however, be pointed out that depression in all but its mildest forms is an illness for which medical help should be sought. Otherwise, the condition can become very severe and can even lead to suicide.

ACUPUNCTURE
This is a traditional Chinese system of medicine based on the Chinese philosophy of yin and yang and aimed at keeping the body in a state of balance. It is thought to have some effect in relieving some of the physical symptoms of depression, such as insomnia, lethargy, lack of appetite, lack of sexual desire and so on.

Treatment involves the insertion of very fine needles a few millimetres into the skin at certain selected points that are grouped along lines know as meridians. These are thought to control the different organs of the body, and the purpose of the needles is to stimulate these meridians so as to re-establish a balanced flow of energy in people whose balance has been disturbed.

As well as inserting the needles, the acupuncturist also tries to establish a good rapport with the patient and tries to encourage him or her to talk things through. The idea is that a combination of needle therapy and encouragement to talk will help the patient to become more balanced and perhaps to take steps to rearrange his or her life with a view to staying well.

HOMOEOPATHY

Homoeopathy is becoming so popular these days that some GPs sometimes recommend homoeopathic remedies, and some are even qualified to practise it.

Homoeopathic medicine is based on giving very small amounts of substances that cause, in a healthy body, the symptoms from which the patient is suffering, with the idea of stimulating the body to fight back against the illness.

HERBAL MEDICINE

This is an ancient system of medicine that uses plants from the fields, woods and hedgerows to cure and to prevent illness. It is, of course, important to consult a qualified herbalist for advice on the appropriate herbs rather than just buy a book on the subject and set out on a country trip with secateurs and basket.

Herbs that have been used throughout the years for depression include St John's wort, which is best used under the supervision of a qualified herbalist. Lemon balm, skullcap, vervain and wild oat are also sometimes recommended in the treatment of depression, but again a qualified herbalist should be consulted as to the use of these and other herbs.

Oriental healers once relied on gotu kola, or hydrocotyle, to treat emotional and mental problems such as depression, especially where there is an accompanying physical weakness.

BACH FLOWER REMEDIES

Bach Flower Remedies are a particular form of herbal remedy that was developed specifically to treat emotional or mental states. Several of these are claimed to have relevance to depression. Before one of the Bach Flower Remedies is selected, time should be taken to go through the relevant literature or professional guidance should be sought. The latter approach is essential if the depression is anything but the mildest of mood disorders.

Bach Flower Remedies are all prepared from the flowers of wild plants, bushes and trees. The system and the thirty-eight remedies were discovered by a London doctor who had practised as a bacteriologist and homoeopath.

The Remedies are taken to restore vitality to someone who is suffering from some form of disorder. They are not aimed at physical complaints but at emotional or mental states that may be related to physical illness and may delay and hamper recovery.

The Bach Flower Remedies are held not to be harmful and to be non habit-forming.

AROMATHERAPY

Some people find that aromatherapy is useful in keeping the spirits up and so averting depression, or even in combating depression when it has set in but is at a very early mild stage.

Aromatherapy is a form of therapy that uses essential oils. These are concentrated liquids that are distilled from parts of certain plants. The flowers, leaves, bark, roots and berries can be used, depending on the particular plant.

It has recently become very popular, although it is in fact a very old form of treatment. Indeed, the use of essential oils goes back to the time of the ancient Egyptians. They had a method of extracting the oils from the relevant plants, most of them fragrant plants, and used these to make ointments and salves that they used for the purpose of healing as well as for embalming the dead. The Egyptians also used the oils in the making of perfumes and in cooking.

The use of essential oils was handed down from the ancient Egyptians to the ancient Greeks and on to the Romans. They were used extensively by the Arab physicians, and some of the oils, and the knowledge of how to distil and use them, were brought back to Europe by the knights who had gone on the Crusades.

The name 'aromatherapy', unlike the concept or the principles behind it, is recent. It is derived from the French word *aromatherapie*, which was coined by René Maurice Gattefosse, a chemist in his family's perfumery business, who discovered the healing and antiseptic properties of some of the oils that he was using in perfumery. He then undertook research into the medical application of aromatherapy and essential oils and published a book on 'aromatherapie' in 1928.

In Britain the interest in aromatherapy is considerably more recent than in France, but it is now very active. It is sometimes made use of in hospitals and in hospices to improve the sense of wellbeing of patients.

The essential oils used in aromatherapy can be used in several ways. They are now quite readily available from herbalists, from some chemists, or from some beauty shops.

Baths

A few drops of the appropriate oil or a few drops of a

mixture of appropriate oils can be added to a hot bath.
The oils then penetrate through the skin to achieve the
desired effect.

Foot baths may also be prepared, using a few drops
of the appropriate essential oil or oils in a bowl of hot
water.

Inhalations

Steam inhalations using the relevant essential oil or
mixture of oils can be used. A few drops of the oil or
the oils are added to a bowl or jug of boiling water, a
towel is placed over the head and the bowl, and the va-
pour is inhaled for a few minutes.

Alternatively, a few drops of the oil or oils can be
sprinkled on a handkerchief and inhaled.

Scenting a room

A few drops of the appropriate oil or oils can be added
to a plant spray, or similar spray, containing water and a
room sprayed with this.

Alternatively, burners can be purchased with a kind
of well at the top for holding a few drops of oil or oils,
often mixed with water. The heat is supplied by a night-
light candle placed in the bottom of the burner.

Massage

All the above applications of essential oils can be carried out by the person who is seeking to achieve the rel-

evant effect. However, massage is one of the most successful and effective ways of using the properties of the essential oils. Although massaging particular parts of the body, such as the feet or legs, can be carried out by the person seeking the therapy, if a whole body massage is desired then obviously someone else has to administer the massage.

The relevant oils are selected, but before they are applied to the skin they must be diluted in a base oil, such as wheat-germ oil, olive oil, grape-seed oil, almond oil or apricot kernel oil, or in a mixture of base oils.

Selection of oils

Essential oils tend to be very fragrant and so very pleasant. It is, therefore, all too easy to forget that they can be very powerful and that considerable knowledge and expertise is necessary in order to use them effectively and without adverse effect. Some essential oils are indeed contra-indicated in certain conditions.

The selection of essential oils is particularly important with relevance to whole-body massage, although it is important in other uses of them as well. People who are contemplating the use of essential oils should therefore seek expert advice.

There are many books published on the subject, and these can supply useful information on the properties of the essential oils and on the use of some essential oils in certain situations. They also indicate those conditions that are likely to be adversely affected by the oil. Of course, it must be borne in mind that some of us have conditions that we might not know about. High blood pressure is such a condition.

Expert advice

However, in view of the fact that essential oils, at least in their most pure forms, are extremely powerful, informed advice should be sought before treatment for a condition such as depression is undertaken. Certainly in the case of massage, where a cocktail of essential oils is often used, expert knowledge, and expert application, are essential.

As is the case with psychotherapy, there is no formal, official qualification for aromatherapists. Even when people appear to have some qualifications it has to be borne in mind that both the length of the training and the quality of the training vary enormously. Some training courses, for example, last only a weekend.

The message, therefore, has to be to shop around until you find someone who appears to have above average qualifications. Ask friends for personal recommendations, see if your local health centre can help, or contact your local library to see if it has any relevant lists or information.

Obviously, people who are suffering from severe depression are unable to do this because their condition deprives them of energy and motivation, but then people who are suffering from severe depression are beyond the help of aromatherapy. It really has relevance only to very mild cases.

Essential oils relevant to depression

The selection of the right essential oils for the situation is particularly important in depression, which can have various aspects and which can have tragic results if it goes untreated. Bergamot, geranium, melissa and rose help lift the mood of depressed people without sedating in any way. Chamomile, clary sage, lavender, sandalwood and ylang ylang are used in cases where sedative and antidepressant properties are called for. Where anxiety is associated with depression, neroli is thought to be effective.

RELAXATION

As has been indicated in Chapter 4, entitled Depression—Causes, no one really has yet got to grips with the causes of depression. However, there is thought often to be more than one cause involved. When there are several factors involved in someone beginning to suffer from depression it is possible that one of these could be stress.

People who are suffering from depression often find it difficult to switch off. Their thoughts race on, usually round and round in an unconstructive way. Relaxation can help people try and avert depression or can be used as therapy, at least in the early stages of depression before it becomes severe. It can also be used as back-up therapy during another course of treatment. For example, it might be useful during drug therapy while the drugs are reaching their peak effectiveness.

In our fast, tense, stress-filled world people have to learn to relax. Relaxation is not simply slumping in front of the television watching the soaps. It is a method of emptying our minds of all the impedimenta that is gathered there and of easing the tension in our bodies.

Relaxation techniques vary with the preference of the individual, and it is important for anyone who is interested in relaxation to find the method that is right for him or her. Some people find it easy to relax. Others find it extremely difficult, often thinking that they have no time for such a pursuit and often imagining that they will find it boring since they assume, quite wrongly, that deep relaxation is essentially a zombie-like state in which your level of consciousness is markedly dimmed.

Getting ready to relax

Generally, people, especially those who are just beginning to learn relaxation techniques, like to find a comfortable position, although not a position that induces sleep, in order to be able to relax. Such a position varies from person to person. For example, some like to lie on the floor and others prefer to lean back in a comfortable chair. As long as you are comfortable, but not too comfortable, it really does not matter. People who have mastered the art of relaxation after much practice can go into their relaxation routine anywhere, but there is no point in putting obstacles in your way to begin with.

Comfort should also be considered when choosing clothes for relaxation sessions. Loose and comfortable clothing is considerably more conducive to relaxation than the rather tight suit that you may have worn to the office. If you are trying to slough off the worries of the day, you are less likely to achieve your aim if you are constantly aware of the tightness of your waistband.

It is important deliberately to set aside some time each day for your relaxation session. We all know how easy it is to have good intentions but somehow never find the time to carry these out. A little self-discipline is necessary to make some time for oneself, and it is easier to do this on a regular basis rather than simply snatch a few minutes at a different time each day, at least until your relaxation session becomes a central part of your life. Again, people who are experienced in relaxation techniques can snatch a few minutes anywhere to go into their routine and de-stress themselves, but it takes some considerable time to achieve such expertise.

If you are just embarking on a relaxation programme, it is also important to provide yourself with somewhere quiet and private to set about the process. Until you have learnt something about the art of switching off, it is not fair to yourself to try out your relaxation technique in busy or noisy surroundings. It is all too easy to become distracted and then to assume that you are not a suitable candidate for relaxation. In time you may become one of those lucky people who can go into a relaxation programme anywhere, no matter how noisy or stressful your surroundings are, but it is rather foolish to assume that you will be able to do this right away.

Physical considerations must be thought of if you are contemplating a relaxation programme. Not only does clothing, place and time have to be considered but also the state of one's stomach. If you have just eaten a very heavy meal and go into your relaxation technique, you are very likely to fall asleep. On the other hand, if you have not eaten all day and are absolutely ravenous, you will very likely find it difficult to take your mind off your hunger long enough to concentrate on your relaxation technique.

Time, space, clothing and the state of the stomach are important to the person embarking on a relaxation programme, but there are other things that will help would-be relaxers to achieve their aim. One of these is a concentration on breathing techniques. Most of us, although we are probably unaware of the fact, have a shallow, erratic breathing pattern, in keeping with our

busy, erratic lives. Controlled, regular breathing, however, is important both in relaxation and meditation.
Apart from anything else, it induces a sense of calm
that is central to both of these.

Breathing techniques

In order to master the breathing techniques used in relaxation and meditation programmes, it is worth becoming aware of the timing of the four-second breath,
which is the basis of many breathing techniques. You
breathe in to a count of four and breathe out to a count
of four, often holding the breath at the top of the lungs
to a count of two in between breathing in and breathing
out, and holding the lungs empty to the count of two in
between breathing out and breathing in again. If you
practise this a few times by the clock, you will learn to
judge the timing without recourse to a clock or watch
and will be able to perform automatically the breathing
techniques based on the four-second sequence.

Concentration on breathing directs one's thoughts
away from the day's concerns and problems and ena-
bles one to concentrate purely on oneself. Perhaps the
best-known example of using breathing techniques to
induce relaxation and to divert concentration from
problems, or in this particular case pain, is its use in
natural childbirth. Expectant mothers are taught a series of regular breathing techniques at antenatal classes
so that they might put these into practice during labour

and so decrease their pain levels and the levels of drugs that are otherwise necessary.

Muscular relaxation techniques

Breathing techniques are thus an important part of thought-control or concentration-direction. Another effective way to accomplish this is by muscular relaxation techniques. This involves concentration on parts of the body in turn, for example, on the legs, and on how to recognize tension and relaxation in the muscles related to these. Total relaxation occurs when you are able to concentrate on the whole body, part by part, getting each part to relax. As with concentration on breathing, concentration on relaxed muscles or parts of the body helps to direct one's concentration away from the problems and pressures of one's life.

Getting information

Obviously, there is more to advanced relaxation than can be described here. For anyone interested in the subject, however, there is a great deal of help available. There are various books on the subject obtainable either from your public libraries—although these are so popular now that you may have to reserve them—or from bookshops. Also there are various classes and courses run throughout the country so that people can acquire the essential techniques of relaxation that they can then practise by themselves.

Whether or not you join a class is a matter of personal preference. Some people find that it helps them to get started on something if they make the commitment to join a class. Others find it more difficult to follow written instructions given in a book than spoken instructions given by a teacher or class leader. Both such groups will obviously opt for a class, but many others are quite happy to follow written instructions at home at their own pace, perhaps seeking the advice of a friend with some knowledge of the subject.

Some people who opt for the home-based situation find that relaxation tapes are extremely helpful. These are readily available, and many of them talk would-be relaxers through relaxation techniques or a whole relaxation programme. A degree of self-discipline and concentration is required to get started on such a tape scheme, it being all to easy to buy the tape and put it in a drawer or to use it for a few minutes, get diverted and decide that it is not for you. People who persist with them, however, tend to swear by them, at least in the early stages of their relaxation programmes, when they are in need of a kick-start routine. Others claim that they find such tapes annoying and even patronizing. As with most things in life, the tapes tend to vary in quality.

Some people not only master the art of relaxation and find it effective but go on to practise yoga. Many people who have suffered from depression find this a

good way to relax and unwind, and nowadays there are
many courses and classes in this throughout the country.

PHYSICAL EXERCISE

Many people find that physical exercise can be of value
in depression. Those who suffer from regular bouts of
depression sometimes find that they can ward it off, at
least for a while, by taking some brisk exercise, while
those who are in the recovery process often find that
exercise can speed up this process.

Physical exercise can also be therapeutic in cases of
mild depression, while the sufferer is still in the grip of
the condition. However, it is not really a possibility in
cases of severe depression, since the condition deprives
people of energy, interest and motivation. Just getting
around is a big enough challenge for the sufferer from
severe depression.

The kind of physical exercise indulged in is up to the
individual preference of the person concerned. To be
effective it should be brisk rather than leisurely—brisk
walking and cycling are ideal—and if it is done outside
then the person undertaking the exercise also gets the
benefit of the air.

Physical exercise also has the merit of helping people to sleep better. This is important in depression, if
the initial inertia can be overcome, because sleep disturbance or insomnia is apt to happen.

DIET

It has been indicated in Chapter 4, entitled Depression—Causes, that one possible cause, or at least a contributory cause, of depression is thought to be vitamin or mineral deficiency. Some claims have also been made that particular foods or substances, such as caffeine, can also cause depression if taken in excess, but these claims are difficult to substantiate.

Anyone trying to avoid or ward off depression should eat a good, healthy balanced diet, as indeed we all should. Nowadays, much emphasis is placed on the importance of eating considerable quantities of fruit and vegetables, as these are thought to be powerful allies in the fight against disease.

Depression often brings with it a loss of appetite, although less often it can be accompanied by a desire to overeat. It is important for people suffering from depression to try to eat a balanced diet, however disinclined they are to eat, to keep up their physical strength. It is, of course, difficult to convince severely depressed people of this, since they have little interest in anything.

People prone to depression should avoid more than moderate quantities of alcohol. Contrary to popular belief, alcohol is a depressant. We may feel we are much more cheerful after a glass or two of wine, but this feeling is true of the initial stages of drinking only. Significant quantities of alcohol can make us feel very low even if we are not actually suffering from depression.

SELF-HELP

It is very important that depression is correctly diagnosed and correctly treated. In all but the most mild
cases professional help is needed to cure depression.
However, sufferers from depression can take some
courses of action to help themselves.

Some of these possible courses of action have already been discussed. They include brisk exercise, the
taking of a balanced diet, and learning to relax. Another
course of action involving self-help was described in
Chapter 5, entitled Depression—Treatment, and involves the joining of a self-help group. However, there
are other things that a person who has suffered from
depression, who is in the course of recovering from depression, or who is prone to depression can do to try to
stay well.

Make time for yourself

Too often our overcrowded, fast-paced lives leave us
little time for ourselves. This is often particularly true
of women who are trying to juggle jobs, housekeeping
and parenting. Yet we should be sure to make time for
ourselves, time to do the things we enjoy, time to spend
with the people we like or love, time to admire the
beauty of the countryside, time to sit and think, or time
simply to sit.

Very often people who are prone to depression are
low in self-esteem. Indeed one of the symptoms of de-

pression is low self-esteem falling to a sense of total worthlessness in severe depression. Therefore it is important to remind yourself that you matter—to others and to yourself.

Given the nature of depression, there is probably no point in telling yourself this if you are in the grip of a severe depression. However, you can tell this to yourself if you are in the recovery phase or if you are trying to avoid or ward off depression.

Enjoy yourself

It is important for all of us to spoil ourselves a bit. We should leave time for the things that bring us pleasure, whatever these are—going to the theatre, watching football, gardening, DIY, playing tennis, travelling, driving, whatever suits you

I know several people who have recovered from severe depression who have spoken of the great joy that they experienced when their concentration came back enough to allow them to read a book or to do the crossword. Others have spoken of experiencing similar feelings of joy when they were first able to enjoy listening to music again.

Creative activities

Many people find great pleasure in doing something creative. This satisfies the need that we all have to express ourselves and might be useful in averting depression or in aiding the recovery stage.

Trying something new is always a good thing. It does not matter what form the creativity takes, whether it be painting, composing poetry, writing the novel that is meant to be inside all of us, playing a musical instrument, embroidery, tapestry—there is much to choose from. An important thing to remember is not to impose too high standards on yourself in the course of your creative activity. It does not matter how bad or good you are at the activity. What is important is that you derive pleasure from doing it.

Communication

Isolation can be at least a contributory cause of depression. It is, therefore, important, to keep in touch with people. This does not mean simply seeing people and exchanging stock greetings in the course of our daily lives. It means really talking to people, having conversations with friends and family, preferably face to face, otherwise by telephone, meeting new people, exchanging opinions and ideas. Keeping oneself to oneself is simply not a good idea, especially if one is in any way prone to depression.

Express your feelings

The leaflet on depression published by the Royal College of Psychiatrists and the Royal College of General Practitioners encourages people who are being treated for depression not to 'bottle things up'. It advises people who have had some bad news or a major upset in their lives to talk about it or 'to have a good cry'.

Often people who are prone to depression find it difficult to cry and publicly to show their pain and hurt. Yet it is far better to weep than to internalize the hurt and pain, something that can contribute to the onset of depression, especially if the cause of the hurt and pain is a major life event, such as bereavement.

Showing and receiving demonstrations of affection are good things also. Too many of us do not take time to give a hug to the people who matter to us. Yet a hug can indicate much more than words.

The comfort of a pet

People who are prone to depression and who live alone should think about getting a pet, such as a cat or dog. Stroking a pet can be very therapeutic when you are feeling down, and having to walk a dog makes sure that you get out of the house and take some exercise.

Emphasis is often placed on how much trouble pets are, but those who have them will tell you that the rewards they bring far outweigh the disadvantages.

Doctors and other members of the caring professions have become aware of the importance of pets in the care of the elderly. Some nursing homes even have pets who visit on a regular basis.

Chapter 7

Depression—The Consequences

The consequences of depression can be quite severe for the person who is suffering from the depression, for that person's family and friends, and it has wider implications for society.

PERSONAL DISTRESS

There is, of course, the personal distress endured by the person who is suffering from depression. If anything, the distress suffered by someone who is suffering from depression but who does not know that this is what is causing the mental and emotional changes that are being experienced is worse than the distress caused by the condition.

People who are suffering from severe undiagnosed depression often feel that they are losing their minds and that there will be no cure for this. Thus, it is extremely important that we all become more aware of the nature of depression in order that the distress of undiagnosed depression becomes a thing of the past.

SUICIDE

Very sadly, several people commit suicide while in the grip of severe depression. Severe depression brings to the sufferers black despair, a deep sense of worthlessness and a conviction that the world in general, and their families in particular, would be much better off without them.

It is, of course, not possible to know the exact state of mind of someone who has committed suicide, even in cases where a suicide note is left. However, it seems likely that some of the people who commit suicide do so because they think that they have some terrible incurable disease of the mind rather than depression, which is, in many cases, perfectly curable. Indeed, sometimes their fear could be that they have a terminal physical disease, a conviction that is one of the possible symptoms of depression, and wish to save their families the pain of watching their slow death.

Whatever the distorted thinking behind individual suicides, it is extremely important that society in general takes suicide more seriously than it does at the moment. There is a common belief, and one that is in fact a myth, that people who talk about suicide never actually carry it out.

This may be true of someone who is making a melodramatic statement in response to some rather trivial event that has just happened, and even then one cannot be sure, but it is certainly not true of people who commit suicide when they are suffering from depression. Negative and suicidal thoughts are some of the symptoms connected with severe depression and sometimes these are communicated to friends.

Suicide rarely occurs without there having been any warning signs. The majority of people who commit suicide contact their family doctor during the month prior to the suicidal act, and many have indicated in some way, perhaps by speaking of suicide or by something in their behaviour, that they are thinking of killing themselves.

Another myth that relates to suicide is that people who make an unsuccessful attempt, or several unsuccessful attempts, on their own lives never actually commit suicide. In fact 40 per cent of those who commit suicide have a history of failed attempts, known as parasuicide.

Suicide statistics

The statistics relating to suicide and depression make for very worrying reading. Anthony Clare in *Depression And How To Survive It* (1993) points out that one in seven people who suffer from a major depressive disorder commit suicide.

He also reports the findings of two follow-up studies of people who had been severely depressed. In one of these studies, which was a two-year follow-up of 1000 people who had been hospitalized with depression, 25 people out of a thousand were found to have committed suicide. In the other study, which was a ten-year follow-up of 954 people who had suffered from depression, 68 people out of 954 had committed suicide during the ten-year period.

The suicide rate in England and Wales is also higher than most people would expect. About one per cent of deaths in England and Wales each year are due to suicide, making a rate of 8 people per 100,000 of the population. This, in fact, may be an underestimation since it is not always absolutely clear whether or not someone has committed suicide.

Where there is any doubt whatsoever, or even in cases where there is no real doubt but no actual evidence, the death is not usually put down to suicide. This is partly because it saves the family a lot of pain and distress. It may also be in part a throwback to the time pre-1961 when suicide or attempted suicide was officially regarded as a crime and to the fact that until recently insurance companies would not pay out on life assurance policies if the person whose life was insured had committed suicide—some older policies may still carry such a clause.

The statistics given in *How To Heal Depression* (1995) by Harold H. Bloomfield and Peter McWilliams give no cause for comfort either. They indicate that 15 per cent of all depressed people will commit suicide as a result of their condition and that two-thirds of all suicides are directly related to depression. The authors are American and the book was first published in America and so these figures relate to American statistics.

Distress of relatives of suicides

It is obviously a terrible waste of life when someone commits suicide, but at least the person who has taken such destructive action is not around any more to have to put up with the censure. Censure there certainly is, and it is the person's close family who have to put up with the it.

We have seen that a considerable number of people who commit suicide do so when they are suffering from a severe depressive illness. Yet others kill themselves when they are suffering from some other form of mental illness.

Unfortunately, many members of the public do not know this, and they are apt to blame the person who has taken his or her own life. They see it as an enormous act of cowardice, seeing it simply as an escape from responsibilities, a kind of cop-out.

Relatives are already distressed by the loss of a loved one. They are probably also wracked with guilt that they did not do anything to prevent the suicide, although there might well not have been anything that they could do. On top of this they have to bear the censure that is being heaped on the memory of their relative.

As well as the censure of the public, there is the stigma of suicide for the relatives to bear. Mental illness still carries a stigma, but it is not as bad as that carried by suicide, which still has overtones of being a sin, from the days when suicides were not allowed to be buried in churchyards, and also overtones of crime, from the days before 1961 when it was still a crime in the UK.

It is often the case that relatives, as well as being grief-stricken, also feel some anger, although in fact this anger is unreasonable. For example, if a husband and wife have been experiencing serious financial difficulties and he suffers from severe depression before finally killing himself, it is quite common, at least at first, for the wife to blame her husband for dying and leaving her to bear the whole burden.

Something that can make the death even harder for the relative to bear is the fact that someone who is suffering from depression may quite possibly commit suicide not at the most severe point of depression, when it might be more expected, but when he or she appeared to be just beginning to recover. This is accounted for by the fact that people might have been too fatigued or indecisive to carry out the act when they were at the height of the illness, and it was only when their energy levels began to recover that they were able to muster the reserves to do so.

Friends, too, can suffer several forms of anguish

when someone commits suicide. There is the sad loss of a friend, there is the guilty feeling that perhaps one could have done something to prevent it, and there are often feelings of uncertainty. These arise because often relatives do not tell anyone outside the family circle the circumstances of the death. This is a result of the general attitude towards suicide and a result of the stigma attached to it. Friends are left suspecting, but not really knowing, and therefore often being unable to express their sorrow adequately.

Age, depression and suicide

A fact relating to depression that is of relevance to society generally but is not generally known is that depression is quite common among the elderly. Furthermore, when depression does occur in the elderly it is often very severe, and there is more of a tendency to commit suicide.

One quarter of severely depressed people over the age of sixty-five will commit suicide, compared with one in seven of severely depressed people in the general population.

DIAGNOSIS IN THE ELDERLY

As has been indicated earlier in the book, there is a major problem generally relating to the diagnosis of depression. In the elderly this problem of diagnosis is even worse.

This is because some of the symptoms of depression, such as memory loss, poor concentration and sleep problems, can all too easily be put down to old age, without anyone investigating further. Signs of a depressed mood may be less evident in the elderly than they are in younger people.

With treatment, elderly people recover from depression well, but many of them never get the chance to do so. One of the worst problems concerning depression in the elderly is that the symptoms sometimes get confused with those of dementia or even Alzheimer's disease.

Depression and Alzheimer's disease share some symptoms, such as memory impairment, and confusion but, of course, depression is curable and Alzheimer's disease is not. It is incredibly sad when the two are wrongly confused and the depression goes untreated.

This has implications for all of us since most of us at some point in our lives come into contact with an elderly person, whether this be a grandparent, a parent, a friend or a neighbour. It is up to us to try to make sure that he or she is not wrongly diagnosed and goes on suffering from something that is curable.

DEPRESSION AND THE WORKPLACE
Obviously suicide is the worst possible outcome of depression, but there are problems for those who recover and live. Some of these are job-related.

Many people actually lose their jobs when they are suffering from undiagnosed depression. Several of the symptoms associated with depression affect people's ability to do their work properly. These include loss of concentration, memory impairment and indecisiveness. If the depressed person's work is badly affected, this can easily lead to him or her being dismissed.

Alternatively, people suffering from depression may resign, feeling that they cannot do their jobs. They are unaware that their lack of concentration, memory loss and indecisiveness are part of an illness that is curable. They just know that they cannot go on not coping and they resign, an action that they regret later when they are better.

When people recover from depression they have no job to return to if they have been sacked or if they have resigned. In the present employment situation they are unlikely to be taken back unless they have an unusually understanding employer or unless they are outstandingly, practically uniquely, good at their jobs.

Given the high rate of unemployment at the moment, it is far from easy for people who have recovered from depression to get back into the workplace. In addition, they may have quite unfairly built up a reputation for being poor workers when they were in fact ill. This can result in them receiving bad or indifferent references, which will prevent them from making much progress in the job market.

Stigma

People who have either lost their jobs or given them up while they were depressed often find it difficult to obtain other jobs after they recover because they have been suffering from a form of mental illness and because of the stigma that is still attached to this. The stigma is even worse if the depression has gone undiagnosed for so long and reached such a degree of severity that the depressed person has had to be admitted to a mental hospital.

All this not only has an effect on depressed people's career prospects and on their economic future but also on their general state of mind. There they are, feeling really good about themselves, and then their confidence is shattered when they cannot find a job.

Of course, if the depressed people have dependants, they have to suffer the economic deprivation as well, having already suffered the emotional and mental trauma of living with someone who has been suffering from severe depression. These combined circumstances can put a severe strain on relationships.

DEPRESSION AND RELATIONSHIPS

People are not really themselves when they are suffering from depression, and allowances have to be made for this. They can behave oddly and say things that they do not mean. They make appointments and do not turn up. They change from being amusing people to being melancholy and no fun at all. A whole host of other things may occur.

Unfortunately, people who come into contact with people who are suffering from depression rarely make allowances for them. Either they do not know what is wrong with them or they do not understand the implications and symptoms of the condition.

Family relationships and depression

Feuds can start in families when someone is depressed, and these are sometimes never resolved. It seems odd that other family members would not forgive and forget when the depressed person gets better and when it is appreciated that he or she has been ill. It is a sad fact, however, that this does often happen. Things said and actions carried out can take a long time to be forgotten, even when the person doing the saying and acting was ill at the time.

Friends and depression

Friends can easily fall out when one of them is depressed. People who are depressed are often irritable and can act in ways in which they would not act if they were well, and this can have an adverse effect on friendships.

Friendship is a two-way thing, and depressed people are often bad at getting in touch with people if they are feeling too fatigued. This can easily be misconstrued by friends as not wanting their company, as can the depressed person refusing invitations, again because of fatigue and partly out of lack of motivation.

Depressed people's friends often become annoyed when they keep not turning up for appointments, not realizing that this is part of an illness. Sadly, also, friends sometimes take to avoiding people who are depressed because they tend to go on and on about problems. This is when friends are needed most but they do not know what is going on.

You might expect friends to come together again after things have become clear and the depressed person is well again. Unfortunately this is not always the case and rifts often remain in former friendships.

Spouses and partners and depression

Problems can arise between depressed people and their spouses or partners long before the condition is diagnosed. A lack of interest in sex is an early symptom of depression, but if neither partner knows this it can have a devastating effect on the relationship.

The spouse or partner of the depressed person may well assume that the depressed person has lost interest in their relationship rather than in sex generally. Terrible rows can occur, and the spouse or partner may go off with someone else, without realizing the true situation.

It is not only the sexual element in the relationship

that can go wrong. Depressed people are often irritable, which can give rise to friction. In addition, the change in behaviour and attitude of the depressed person can annoy a spouse or partner because he or she does not know that it is all part of an illness. Where once there was someone lively, energetic and interesting, there is now someone lethargic, dull and always talking about his or her problems.

As is the case with family relationships and friendships, marriages and partnerships can be so badly damaged by depression that they never recover, even after the illness is diagnosed and treated. The spouse or partner may even have left before the diagnosis of illness is made.

CHILDREN AND DEPRESSION

Quite young children can suffer from depression, and children and teachers should be aware of this fact. However, they can also suffer greatly from the depression of an adult.

If the children come from a one-parent family and that parent gets depression the children can be left coping with this burden alone. The parent knows there is something wrong but not what, and the children know there is something wrong but not what. It is even worse for a child who has no siblings and who has to deal with the problem without any help at all.

In fact, young children can be quite badly neglected

by mothers who love them dearly, simply because they are severely depressed. The mothers simply do not have the energy to make sure that everyone has been fed and has clean clothes. There is always the possibility that the social services will misunderstand the situation and take the children into care. This would probably have a disastrous effect on the mother and on the children.

Children often have no idea why their mother is acting the way she is. Children, however, are often very loyal and do everything they can to protect their mother, sometimes even staying off school to look after her and attend to the house.

The worst scenario for the children of a depressed parent is if he or she commits suicide, the depression never having been diagnosed. It is, of course, worse if the children are part of a one-parent family and are left with no one.

Children should not have to live through such things. It is up to us as adults to make sure that they do not. Becoming more aware of the problems that depression in parents can bring to children and knowing more about the condition itself would at least be a start in trying to help them.

CONCLUSION

Depression is a very destructive force. It destroys people, it destroys relationships and friendships, and it destroys careers. Sadly the destruction it creates is often never reversed.

We must, therefore, all become more aware of this destroyer so that we will recognize it, if it occurs in others or in ourselves. Only then will this destructive force, which is in fact a treatable disease, be deprived of its power.

Bibliography

Depression Leaflet issued by The Royal College of Psychiatrists and The Royal College of General Practitioners

Depression And How To Survive It Spike Milligan and Anthony Clare, Arrow Books 1994

How To Heal Depression Dr Harold Bloomfield and Peter McWilliams, Thorsons 1995

Dealing with Depression Gerrilyn Smith and Kathy Nairne The Women's Press, 1984, revised edition 1995

Overcoming Depression Dr Carolyn Shreeve, Thorsons 1984

Defeating Depression Tony Lake Penguin Books, 1987

The Mind Machine Colin Blakemore, BBC Books, 1988

Aromatherapy: An A-Z Patricia Davis, CW Daniel Company Ltd, 1988

Useful Addresses

Association for Post-Natal Illness
25 Jerdan Place
Fulham
London SW6 1BE
Tel 0171 386 0868

British Association for Counselling (BAC)
1 Regent Place
Rugby CV21 2PJ
Tel 01788 578 328

Depressives Anonymous
36 Chestnut Avenue
Beverley
Humberside HU17 9QU

Institute of Complementary Medicine
PO Box 194
London SE16 1QZ
Tel 0171 935 1651

Mind (The National Association for Mental Health)
Granta House
15/19 Broadway
London E15 4BQ
Tel 0181 519 2122

Relate (formerly Marriage Guidance Council)
Head Office
Herbert Gray College
Little Church Street
Rugby CV21 3AP
Tel 01788 573 241

Samaritans
Head Office
10 The Grove
Slough SL1 1QP
Tel 01753 532 713

UK Council for Psychotherapy
Regent's College
Inner Circle
Regent's Park
London NW1 4NS
Tel 0171 487 7554

Index